JEWISH FOLK SONGS
IN YIDDISH AND ENGLISH

COMPILED AND EDITED,
WITH ENGLISH ADAPTATIONS BY RUTH RUBIN

WITH GUITAR ACCOMPANIMENTS BY ETHEL RAIM

OAK PUBLICATIONS, NEW YORK
MUSIC SALES LIMITED, LONDON

ILLUSTRATIONS

The pictures illustrating this song book were carefully chosen to represent first, the various ages, trials and tribulations, ceremonies and festivals, and artists' conceptions of the events that molded the Jewish people; and second, to show the differences of attitudes between the "old world" and the future through the contemporary.

M. A.

Music autography by Carl Rosenthal
Illustrations selected and positioned by Moses Asch
Cover drawing, the Jewish Bride, by Rembrandt
Cover design by Ronald Clyne
Production editor: Ethel Raim

© 1965 Oak Publications 33 West 60th Street, New York 10023

Library of Congress Catalogue Card Number: 65-22692

CONTENTS

PUBLISHER'S FOREWORD

It was at the turn of the present century that the cultural expression of the Jews of Eastern Europe began to be affected by and have an effect upon the larger cultures of the western world. It was a process that was taking place throughout an area of the world that was rapidly changing its ancient ways. Not only the Jewish people but also other minority peoples became exposed in their art and literature to the larger western cultures -- Polish, Russian, French, English.

Yiddish became a language of communication at this time. People developed expressions, idiom and ideas in Yiddish -- and a whole literature of newspapers, plays and books grew up to contain this new expression. The language itself, originally a 17th century German dialect enriched with structures and vocabulary of the Slavic languages, was archaic, but never dormant. It dates back to the break-up of German, Flemish, and the languages of the Netherlands in the Middle Ages.

The life blood of this Jewish expression was nurtured in the hamlets and villages (called the Pale) of Eastern Europe -- and then it developed in the larger cities, such as Warsaw and Kutnow.

The Czars of Russia tried to discourage and destroy this new, budding cultural expression. As part of a program to keep the national minorities of Russia isolated and enslaved, they unleashed the bloody pogroms of the late 19th century. The world was shocked by the bloodshed and persecution -- and from this shock came an awareness that a Jewish people and their culture existed.

At the height of this persecution in the first decade of this century, President Theodore Roosevelt issued a strong protest note to Russia and reminded the world that the United States was a haven for the persecuted and neglected. With this proclamation, the influx of immigrants from Eastern Europe began and a Jewish life started to flourish in the United States.

Soon there were more Yiddish language newspapers in the United States than in Europe. A theater of note thrived, and actors such as Adler, Schildkraut and Muni were recognized as the equals of the best the world had produced. Playwrights, authors and poets created new expressions and ideas in Yiddish.

Eventually all this became part of the "melting pot" and the succeeding generations, without the experience of the persecution and the drive for self-preservation, became a part of the whole world around them.

Ruth Rubin, who put this book together, is herself of a generation at least one step removed from this background. Born in Montreal, she became aware of her heritage at an early age and she has devoted her energy and knowledge to the documentation and preservation of Jewish expression and culture. Today she ranks as one of the outstanding people in the field of social/musical anthropology. Her recording of the European Jewish village songs and expressions of the immigrant generation (Folkways FS3801) is considered one of the important documents in Ethnic Folk Archives.

Moses Asch

Jewish music is diverse and colorful. In their long history in many lands, Jews created several musical cultures and several languages. The Jewish musical treasure embraces songs of Oriental Jews (Yemenite, Sephardic, Persian, Moroccan, Daghestanian, Babylonian); Ladino songs and liturgical melodies of Spaniolic Jews; YIDDISH FOLKSONGS and Chasidic tunes of the East European Jews. Sacred music in the Hebrew tongue (religious folk song) is to be found among Jews the world over, and often differs musically one from the other, depending upon the community in which it is current.

Jewish secular folk song is mainly in the Yiddish vernacular. Whereas a small number of Yiddish folksongs in "archaic" Yiddish trace back to 16th century Western Europe (and even earlier), the bulk of the rich collection of Yiddish folksong relates to the past century and a half in Eastern Europe. These Yiddish folksongs reflect the many-faceted life of the largest Jewish community of modern times, up to World War II, when it was destroyed under German occupation.

During the 80s and 90s of the 19th century, large masses of East European Jews came to our shores, where a rich American-Jewish cultural life was created. Yiddish songs (folk, as well as art, popular and theatrical songs) figured prominently in this development. Although the Yiddish composed songs soon replaced the anonymous folksongs from the "old home", a rich treasure of the old Yiddish folksongs is still alive in the memory of many American Jews of East European origin. In fact, America is one of the most important preservers of Yiddish folksongs today. In Israel, following the establishment of the State in 1948, many aspects of East European Yiddish folksong have been absorbed into Israeli song and music.

This selection of Yiddish songs with singable English translations is a sampling from the many categories of Yiddish folksong. It includes lullabies, children's songs, riddle songs, poverty and work songs, dancing and drinking songs, humorous and nonsense songs, wedding songs, ballads, laments, love songs, courting and conversation songs, soldier songs, struggle songs. It includes also some ten songs of literary origin (by known authors).

Translating folksongs, however, is a serious responsibility. At best, such transmissions or adaptations can only serve as an accommodation and an aid. The translator is faced with the problems of transferring idiomatic expressions, traditional musical subtleties, specific national charm - from one culture to another. Folksongs which may have taken centuries to grow within a specific time and space, often cannot even be transferred adequately to another culture, which has had its own history and development in an entirely different time and place. Yet, translations from one language to another have always been made, and so, the attempt here was made also!

In doing so, it was my desire to pass on to our young generations, some of the songs of an "old" yesterday, which in their time and place, were once young and alive. These were the songs, which the parents and grandparents of many Americans brought with them to our land, when, in their own youth some generations ago, they hopefully came to build, with their sweat and blood, the institutions, the temples, the edifices, the diverse patterns of life, which we all enjoy today.

May this songbook help a little, to bridge the gap between the generations and may ALL enjoy singing the Yiddish folksongs of my people!

Ruth Rubin

Amol Iz Geven a Mayse

The Jews They Had a King

Lullaby. English text by Ruth Rubin, © 1964 by Appleseed Music, Inc.

A - mol iz ge-ven a may-se. Di may-se iz gor-nit frey-lech. Di
The Jews they had a king, — So ve-ry long a-go, —

may - se hoybt zich o - net Mit a yi-dish-n mey-lech.
This is how the sto-ry be-gins my love, But it ends in woe.—

Lyu - lin-ke mayn fey-ge-le, Lyu - lin-ke mayn kind.
Hush my lit-tle ba - by, Hush my lit-tle bir - die,

Ch'ob on-ge-voy-rn a-za li - be. Vey iz mir un vind. —
I have lost my own true love, Woe is un-to me. —

Amol iz geven a mayse,	The Jews they had a king
Di mayse is gornit freylech,	So very long ago,
Di mayse hoybt zich onet,	This is how the story begins, my love,
Mit a yidishn meylech.	But it ends in woe...
Refrain:	Refrain:
Lyulinke, mayn feygele,	Hush my little baby,
Lyulinke, mayn kind.	Hush my little birdie,
Chob ongevoyrn aza libe,	I have lost my own true love,
Vey iz mir un vind!	Woe is unto me!
Der meylech hot gehat a malke,	The king he had a queen so fair,
Di malke hot gehat a vayngortn,	The queen she had a vineyard rare,
Der vayngortn hot gehat a boym,	The vineyard had a very old tree,
Lyulinke, mayn kind. (Ref.)	Hush my little baby. (Ref.)

Der boym hot gehat a tsvayg,
Der tsvayg hot gehat a nestele,
In nestele iz geven a feygele,
Lyulinke, mayn kind. (Ref.)

Der meylech iz opgeshtorbn,
Di malke iz gevorn fardorbn,
Der tsvayg iz opgebrochn,
Dos feygele fun nest antlofn. (Ref.)

Vu nemt men aza chochem,
Er zol kenen di shtern tseyln?
Vu nemt men aza dokter,
Er zol kenen mayn harts heyln? (Ref.)

A branch grew on that very old tree,
In a nest on the branch, sat a little
   birdie,
The birdie chirped so hungrily,
Hush my little baby. (Ref.)

The king died suddenly one day,
The queen, she mourned and pined away,
The branch broke off that tree, my love,
And the birdie flew away. (Ref.)

Oh, where is the man so wondrous wise,
Who can count all the stars in the deep
   blue sky?
Oh, where is the doctor, where is he?
To heal that broken heart of me? (Ref.)

Af Di Felder, Grine Felder

Over the Greenwood, on the Plain

Soldiers lament, collected by Ruth Rubin. English text by Ruth Rubin. © 1964, by Appleseed Music, Inc.

(Music notation, key of E minor, chords: Em, B7, Em, G, Em, Am, B7, Em)

Af di fel-der, gri-ne fel-der, Oy vey.
O-ver the green-wood on the plain, — oh, oh.

Af di fel-der, gri-ne fel-der, Dort ligt far-vor-fn a yun-ger zel-ner,
O-ver the green-wood on the plain — Lies a sol-dier in bat-tle slain —

oy — vey! Dort ligt far-vor-fn a yun-ger zel-ner oy — vey!
oh _____ Lies a sol-dier in bat-tle slain __ oh. _____

Af di felder, grine felder, oy, vey,
Af di felder, grine felder,
Dort ligt farvorfn a yunger zelner, oy, véy
Dort ligt farvorfn a yunger zelner, oy, vey

Kumt a foygl on tsu fli-en, oy, vey.
Af zayn keyver optsu-ri-en, oy, vey.

Oy, du foygl, fli geshvind.
Un zog der mamen, ich bin gezint.

Fun dem toyt zolstu ir nit zogn.
Vayl zi vet nebech veynen un klogn.

Kumt der foygl tsu fli-en aheym.
Un treft zayn mamen troyerig shteyn.

Vey iz mir, oy vey un vind.
M'hot fartribn mayn eyntsig kind.

Ven di zamd vet tserinen vern.
Vet zich tsu mir mayn kind umkern.

Ven di zamd vet amol antrinen.
Ir kind vet shoyn aheym nit kimen.

Over the greenwood on the plain, oh, oh.
Over the greenwood on the plain,
Lies a soldier in battle slain, oh,
Lies a soldier in battle slain, oh.

A lonely bird comes swooping low.
Resting upon his tender brow.

Bird fly swiftly down the dell.
Tell my mother I am well.

Do not tell her that dead am I.
Bitterly she'll moan and cry.

Away the bird flew to his home.
And found his mother all alone.

Thinking only of her son.
"Where are you now, beloved one?"

When the sands will drift away.
My son from war returns that day.

Alas, the sands will drift away.
Her son will not return that day.

Ale Vasserlech Flisn Avek

All the Rivers Flow Down to the Sea

Lament collected by Ruth Rubin, English text by Ruth Rubin. © 1964 by Appleseed Music, Inc.

A - le vas-ser-lech fli - sn a - vek. Di gri - be-lech
All the riv-ers flow down to the sea. The ditch-es are

blay - bn ley - dig. Ni - to a - za mentsh oyf
emp - ty and dry. There's not a sin-gle soul to

gor der velt. Vos zol far -shteyn mayn vey - tig.
lis - ten to me, No one to hear my sad cry.

Ale vasserlech flisn avek,
Di gribelech blaybn leydig.
Nito aza mentsh oyf gor der velt
Vos zol farshteyn mayn veytig.

Di yorelech tsi-en, di yorelech fli-en,
Di tsayt geyt avek vi roych.
Un az ich dermon zich on dir, mayn zis-lebn,
Geyt mir oys der koyech.

Un az a meydele shpilt a libe,
Shpiln in ir ale farbn.
Un az zi shpilt ir libe nit oys,
Kon zi cholile noch shtarbn.

Un az di tepelech trikenen oys,
Blaybn zey ale leydig.
Un az a meydele firt ir libe nit oys,
Vert zi farfaln oyf eybig.

All the rivers flow down to the sea,
The ditches are empty and dry.
There's not a single soul to listen to me,
No one to hear my sad cry.

My youth has come and now it has
vanished,
I am left so ashamed and alone.
When I recall the days, when we both
loved so tenderly,
I sit and I weep and I moan.

When a young girl falls in love,
Her cheeks are so rosy and fair,
But when a man breaks her heart and
then he leaves her,
She can die of despair.

A jilted girl is an empty vessel,
A jug that was once filled with wine,
Oh, to have loved so well and then to
have lost you,
To be doomed to weep and to pine.

A Geneyve

The Robbery

This nonsense song, typical of other taunts and cumulative humorous songs created by the cheder-boys, points up the abysmal poverty of their enviorment, and especially of their teacher, the rebe.

English Text by Ruth Rubin, ©1964, by Appleseed Music, Inc.

Bay mayn re-bn iz ge-ve-zn, Iz ge-ve-zn
A thief got in-to, yes, broke in-to, My poor rab-bi's

bay mayn re-bn, Bay mayn re-bn iz ge-ve-zn
house, got in-to, He broke in-to Yes, in-to my

a ge-ney-ve! Zi-on hem-der vi di be-cher,
poor rab-bi's house._ What do you think he found there, stole there?

Dray mit la-tes, fir mit le-cher. Bay mayn re-bn
Sev-en old shirts of worn-out wool there, Three had patch-es,

iz ge-ve-zn, A ge-ney-ve!
four had holes there, Boy, what a haul! _

Refrain:

Bay mayn rebn iz gevezn,
Iz gevezn bay mayn rebn,
Bay mayn rebn iz gevezn:
A geneyve!

Zibn hemder vi di becher,
Dray mit lates, fir mit lecher,
Bay mayn rebn iz gevezn,
A geneyve! (Ref.)

Zibn laychter vi di bern,
Dray on fis un fir on rern,
Bay mayn rebn iz gevezn,
A geneyve! (Ref.)

Refrain:

A thief got into, yes, broke into,
My poor rabbi's house, got into
He broke into, yes, into my
Poor rabbi's house!

What do you think he found there, stole
   there?
-Seven old shirts of good old wool there,
Three had patches, four had holes there,
-Boy, what a haul! (Ref.)

What else do you think he found there?
  Seven candelabra, stole there,
Four - no sockets, three - no legs there,
-Boy, what a haul! (Ref.)

Zibn hener vi di tsigl,
Dray on kep un fir on fligl,
Bay mayn rebn iz gevezn,
A geneyve! (Ref.)

Zibn techter vi di sosnes,
Dray on tseyn un fir on yosles,
Bay mayn rebn iz gevezn,
A geneyve! (Ref.)

Grabbed seven roosters, red as bricks there,
Without heads and without beaks there,
Out the window, then he flew there -
Boy, with his haul! (Ref.)

Took the rabbi's seven daughters,
Tall and toothless, all in tatters,
Maidens all, what did it matter?
-Boy, what a haul! (Ref.)

Aylye Lyulye Lyulye

This traditional lullaby reveals the role of the working mother, who supported her males (husbands, sons) in the Jewish Pale in Eastern Europe of a century and more ago. In harmony with the mores of that time, she was making it possible for them to spend their life as scholars and pious men, thus raising the status of the family as a whole. In an environment where scholarship and piety were of primary importance, this gave the family prestige in this world and helped assure their entry into Paradise in the afterlife as well...

English text by Ruth Rubin, © 1964 by Appleseed Music, Inc.

Ay - lye   lyu - lye   lyu   lye   Shlof-zhe shlof mayn   g'du - le,
Ay - li   lu - li   lu   li   Sleep my pre-cious   ba - by,

Mach-zhe   tsu   day - ne   ey - ge - lech di   fay - ne.
Close your pret-ty   eyes   Close your love - ly   eyes.

Ay lye lyu lye lyu lye
Shlof-zhe, shlof mayn g'dule,
Mach-zhe tsu dayne
Eygelech di fayne.

Un shtey oyf vider,
Mit gezunte glider,
Mayn lib-zis kind,
Gich un geshvind.

In mark vel ich loyfn,
Beygelech vel ich koyfn,
Mit puter vel ich shmirn,
Tsu der chupe zol ich dich firn...

Vest oysvaksn a groysinker,
Vestu zayn a tane!
Veln doch ale
Zayn mich mekane!

Ay li lu li, lu, li,
Sleep my precious baby,
Close your pretty eyes,
Close your lovely eyes.

When you wake up by and by,
You'll be healthy, you'll be spry,
Now you must go to sleep,
Now you must go to sleep.

I will hurry to the square,
Get some fresh rolls for you there,
I'll butter them for you,
Find a sweet bride for you too...

You'll be a scholar of renown,
The wisest man in all the town,
For your piety,
Everyone will envy me!

Bin Ich Mir a Shnayderl

I Am a Little Tailor

A sardonic conversation song, which first presents the "busy little craftsmen" of the poverty-stricken little backwoods towns of the Jewish Pale – as happy at their work. Then, it proceeds, to the rhythm of a gay wedding-dance tune, to tell us the truth of the widespread, hopeless poverty.

English text by Ruth Rubin, © 1964 by Appleseed Music, Inc.

Bin ich mir a shnay-der-l,
I am a lit-tle tai-lor, day-di-dam.
Bin ich mir a shnay-der-l,
I am a lit-tle tai-lor, day-di-di.

Leb ich mir tog-oys, tog-ayn,
I stitch and sew the live-long day, I am

Lus-tig un frey-lech un fayn.
jol-ly and as hap-py as can be.

Zog mir shnay-der,
Tell me lit-tle tai-lor, li-bin-ker un gu-ter.
bu-sy lit-tle tai-lor, How can you sing gai-ly and mer-ri-ly?

Git dir di no-dl, ge-
Does your lit-tle nee-dle, your flash-ing lit-tle nee-dle

nug oyf broyt mit pu-ter?
Earn e-nough to feed your fa-mi-ly?
Ich mach a voch, tsvey
I work all day, go

gil - dn mit a dray-er,
wea - ri - ly to bed, —

Ich es nor broyt vayl

pu - ter iz tsu tay - er.
dry — crust of bread. —

Bin ich mir a shnayderl (2x)
Leb ich mir tog oys, tog ayn.
Lustig un freylech un fayn.
--Zog mir shnayder, libinker un guter,
  Git dir di nodl genug oyf broyt mit
    puter?
--Ich mach a voch, tsvey gildn mit a
    drayer,
  Ich es nor broyt, vayl puter iz tsu
    tayer.

Bin ich mir a shusterl (2x)
Leb ich mir tog oys, tog ayn,
Lustig un freylech un fayn.
--Zog mir, shuster, hostu vos tsu
    kayen?
  Felt dir oyset, krigstu vu tsu layen?
--Keyner layt nisht, keyner git kayn
    orves,
  Ich bin a shuster, gey ich take borves.

Bin ich mir a blecherl (2x)
Leb ich mir tog oys, tog ayn,
Lustig un freylech un fayn.
--Zog mir blecher, vi groys iz bay dir
    di noyt?
  Hostu bulkes, hostu nit kayn broyt?
--Ich zits un klap bay yenem fremde
    decher,
  Bay mir in shtub rint fun ale lecher.

Bin ich mir a kremerl (2x)
Leb ich mir tog oys, tog ayn,
Lustig un freylech un fayn.
--Zog mir kremer, tsu hostu mit
    vos tsu handlen?
  Hostu in kreml rozhinkes mit mandlen?
--Ich hob in kreml far tsvey groshn
    s'choyre,
  Ich shlep dem dalis, un ich bentsch
    dem boyre.

I am a little tailor, day-di-dam,
I am a little tailor, day-di-di.
I stitch and sew the livelong day,
I am jolly and as happy as can be.
--Tell me little tailor, busy little
   tailor,
   How can you sing gaily and merrily?
   Does your little needle, your flashing
   little needle
   Earn enough to feed your family?
--I work all day, go wearily to bed,
   All that we can get to eat, is a dry
   crust of bread.

I am a little cobbler, day-di-dam.
I am a little cobbler, day-di-di,
I hammer and peg the livelong day,
I am jolly and as happy as can be.
--Tell me little cobbler, eager little
   cobbler,
   What makes you sing so gaily and
   merrily?
   Does your little hammer, your awl
   and little hammer
   Shield you from the curse of poverty?
--My credit's poor, I have no funds for
   spending,
   I cobble other people's shoes, my own
   could stand some mending.

I am a little tinsmith, day-di-dam,
I am a little tinsmith, day-di-di
I fix old roofs the livelong day,
I am jolly and as happy as can be.
--Tell me little tinsmith, nimble little
   tinsmith,
   What makes you sing so gaily and
   merrily?
   Does your labor give you, a fairly
   decent living?
   Does your work give you security?
--I toil all day, fixing houses every-
   where,
   Money's very scarce, my own shack
   leaks and is so bare.

I am a little merchant, day-di-dam,
I am a little merchant, day-di-di,
I trade my wares the livelong day,
I am jolly and as happy as can be.
--Tell me little merchant, pious little
   merchant,
   Have you many things in your little
   shop?
   Do you have some almonds? Do you
   sell sweet raisins?
   Are your shelves filled to the very
   top?
--My shelves are almost empty, may
   the good Lord help us, let us pray,
   Everybody's poor in town, we only
   live from day to day...

Bay Dem Shtetl Shteyt a Shtibl

We Live at the Edge of Town

Children's song. English text by Ruth Rubin, © 1964 by Appleseed Music, Inc.

Bay dem shtet - l, shteyt a shtib - l, Mit a gri - nem dach, ___
We live at the edge of town, In a house so small, ___

Un a - rum dem shti - bl vak - sn bey - me - lech a
The roof is green and all a - round, the lit - tle trees grow

1. Em   **2.** Em

sach. ___ sach.
tall. ___ tall.

Bay dem shtetl shteyt a shtibl Mit a grinem dach, Un arum dem shtibl vaksn Beymelech a sach.	We live at the edge of town In a house so small. The roof is green and all around, the Little trees grow tall.
Un der tate mit der mame, Chanele mit mir, Shoyn a lange tsayt ineynim Voynen ale fir.	Mother, father and my sister Chanele and me, We've been living here a long time, All so happily.
Un der tate, horevet, horevet, Ale yorn zayne. Un er koyft undz, un er brengt undz, Zachn sheyne, fayne.	Father works and works and works But I can clearly see, He buys food and pretty toys For Chanele and me.
Brengt a hintele vos se havket, Mitn nomen Tsutsik. Brengt a ferdl vos se hirzhet, Mitn nomen Mutsik.	He brought a puppy, barking, barking, So we called him Tsutsik. He brought a pony, neighing, neighing. So we called him Mutsik.
Brengt a gendzele mit a langn haldz, Federlech vays vi shney. Brengt a hun vos kvoket, kvoket, Biz zi leygt an ey!	He brought a long-necked goosey, loosey, Her feathers were soft and white, And a hen that cackled, cackled And laid an egg that night.
Nemt di mame, ot di eyer, Ay, iz dos a moyfes! Zetst zi oyf oyf zey a kvoke: Hobn mir naye oyfes!	Mother took the newlaid eggs and She did such a trick! She put them under a setting-hen And we had baby chicks!

Oyfn Yam Veyet A Vintele

Over the Sea the Breezes Are Blowing

As in Bin ich mir gegangen fishelech koyfn, this dancing song seems to conceal its sentiments under a "humorous" cloak. In fact, there are those who interpret it in a broad humorous style.

Love-dancing song. English text by Ruth Rubin, © 1964 by Appleseed Music, Inc.

Oyf - n yam vey - et a vin - te - le, Un _ di chval - yes
O-ver the sea bree-zes are blow - ing, Waves_ do bil-low and

shlo - gn. Ich hob zich far-libt in a sheyn yin-ge-le,
roll. ____ I fell in love with a hand-some young fel - low

Ch'ob nit far ve-men tsu zo - gn.
I dare not con-fide in a soul. ____

Oyfn yam veyet a vintele,	Over the sea, breezes are blowing,
Un di chvalyes shlogn.	Waves do billow and roll.
Ich hob zich farlibt in a sheyn yingele,	I fell in love with a handsome young fellow,
Ch'ob nit far vemen tsu zogn.	I dare not confide in a soul.
Ich hob zich gebovet a shtibele in vald,	I built me a cabin in the green forest,
Arum un arum mit fenster.	With windows of glass all around.
Fun ale kartinkes vos ich hob gezen,	In all this world, of all the pretty pictures,
Biztu bay mir der shenster!	You are the loveliest I have ever found.
Tsu libstu mich fun tifn hartsn,	Tell me you love me with all your heart,
Tsu libstu nor mayn sheyn ponim?	Not alone for my pretty young face -
Du host mich gor avekgekoylet	Oh, you have slain me, with love you have slain me,
Azoy vi di rechte gazlonim!	If you leave me, I'll be ever in disgrace.
Az a gazlen koylet a mentshn,	When a highwayman waylays his victim,
Koylet er im mit a messer.	Money is his only desire -
Host mich gekoylet un nisht derkoylet,	But you have slain me forever and ever,
Bizt fun a gazlen noch gresser!	I am consumed in love's fire.

Bayt-zhe Mir Oys a Finf-un-tsvantsiger

Bandsman, Change My Twenty-Fiver Now

A well-to-do guest at a wedding, keeps tipping the bandsmen to play for him his favorite little tune. The more he dances, the tipsier he seems to get and his feet move slower and slower. His tips too, are becoming smaller...

English text by Ruth Rubin, © 1964 by Appleseed Music, Inc.

Bayt -zhe mir oys a finf - un - tsvan-tsi - ger, Oyf
Bands-men change my twen - ty - fi - ver now,

sa-me-rod - ne dray - er, Un shpilt-zhe mir klez -
In -to pie - ces of three And play for me a jol - ly

mo-rim-lech, A li - de - le, a tay - er.
lit - tle tune, A hap - py dance for me. ___

Refrain:

Rim-tshi rim - tshi, Rim-tshi rim - tshi, Rim-tshi rim - tshi,

1. Rim-tshi rom!   2. Rim-tshi rom!

Bayt-zhe mir oys a finf-un-
  tsvantsiger,
Oyf samerodne drayer,
Un shpilt-zhe mir klezmorimlech,
A lidele a tayer.

Refrain:

Rimtshi (7) rom
Rimtshi (7) rom.

Bandsmen, change my twenty-fiver
  now,
Into pieces of three,
And play for me a jolly little tune,
A happy dance for me.

Refrain:

Rimtshi (7) rom.
Rimtshi (7) rom.

Bayt-zhe mir oys a finf-un-tsvantsiger,
Oyf samerodne firer,
Un shpilt-zhe mir klezmorimlech,
Dos zelbige vi fri-er. (Ref.)

Bayt-zhe mir oys a finf-un-tsvantsiger,
Oyf samerodne tsener,
Un shpilt-zhe mir klezmorimlech,
Dos zelbige noch shener. (Ref.)

Bayt-zhe mir oys a finf-un-tsvantsiger,
Oyf same imperialn,
Ich vel betn di klezmorimlech,
Zey zoln zich nit ayln. (Ref.)

Bandsmen, change this twenty-fiver
   now,
Into pieces of four.
And play that lovely little melody,
As you did before. (Ref.)

Bandsmen, change another twenty-five,
Into pieces of ten,
And play that lovely little wedding dance
Many times again. (Ref.)

Bandsmen, all my money now is spent,
I haven't any more.
But if you play that sweet old tune again—
You'll have to play it slower...(Ref.)

Bin Ich Mir Gegangen Fishelech Koyfn

I Went to Market to Buy Me Some Fish

It is often difficult to categorize this type of Yiddish folksong. Is it a love song? Or a humorous song? Satirical? Dancing? Nonsense? – Actually, it contains elements of all of these types. In the environment of the Czarist Pale of Settlement, with its mores and customs of arranged marriages, love between the sexes prior to marriage, was not acceptable. Consequently, many a love sentiment, hid behind a cloak. The dancing songs, for instance, most often used love themes, which were set to the particular dance rhythm being performed.

In this song, which in the Yiddish version uses the Chasidic refrain of day–day–day, the brisk three-quarter time seems to echo the sounds of hurdy-gurdies at a fair.

English text by Ruth Rubin, © 1964 by Appleseed Music, Inc.

Bin ich mir ge - gang - en fi - she - lech koy - fn,
I went to mar - ket to buy me some fish ___

Hob ich mir ge - koyft ___ a hecht. ___ Un
They had on - ly pick-e-rels that day. ___ May the

ver es iz shul - dig in un - dzer li - be,
vil - lain who stole the love of my heart ___

Der zol oys - geyn vi a lecht!
Pine ___ and with - er a - way. ___

Day - day - day day - day-day day - day - day day - day - day
Life is so brief, my dear, Skies are so sel - dom clear,

Day - day - day day - day-day day - day - day Day.
Cher - ish the hap - py times, When love is near.

Bin ich mir gegangen fishelech koyfn,
Hob ich mir gekoyft a hecht.
Un ver es iz shuldig in undzer libe,
Der zol oysgeyen vi a lecht!

Refrain:

Day (6x) Day (6x)
Day (6x) Day, day, day, day.

Az a kartyozhnik shpilt in kortn,
Farshpilt er doch nor zayn gelt.
Ich hob farshpilt mayne yunge yorn,
Finster iz doch mayn velt. (Ref.)

On kayn tsigl un on kayn shteyner,
Kon men kayn hoyz nisht moyern.
Ay, s'iz nishto aza mentsh oyf der velt,
Vos er zol mich nisht badoyern! (Ref.)

I went to market to buy me some fish
They had only pickerels that day.
May the villain who stole the love of
   my heart
Pine and wither away!

Refrain:

Life is so brief, my dear
Skies are so seldom clear
Cherish the happy times
When love is near.

Day (6x) Day (6x)
Day (6x) day, day, day, day.

When a gambler gambles at cards
He risks all he's got on high stakes.
He loses money, but I lost my true love,
Lordie, how my poor heart breaks.
(Ref.)

Without any bricks, without any stones,
You can't build a house that way –
Oh, good people, hear my sad story,
See how I'm pining away! (Ref.)

Biztu Mit Mir Broygez?

Why Do You Pout and Frown?

Dancing song. English text by Ruth Rubin, © 1964 by Appleseed Music, Inc.

Biz-tu mit mir broy - gez,__ veys ich nit far-vos?
Why do you pout and frown, you are an - gry all day long?

Geyst a-rum a gant-sn tog__ a - rop-ge-lozt di noz.
Speak to me my dear young wife __ What have I done wrong?

Refrain: Day day day day day day, Day day day day.
Day day day day day day, Day day day day.

Geyst a-rum a gant-sn tog__ a - rop-ge-lozt di noz.
Speak to me my dear young wife __ what have I done wrong?

Biztu mit mir broygez,
Veys ich nit farvos?
Geyst arum a gantsn tog
Aropgelozt di noz.

Refrain:

Day-day-day, etc.

Un efsher vilstu visn
Az ich hob dich lib?
Lomir beyde ariberforn
Tsu dem gutn yid. (Ref.)

Tsu dem gutn yidn,
A pidyen im opgebn.
Vet er far undz got betn
Far a gut lebn. (Ref.)

Why do you pout and frown?
You are angry all day long.
Speak to me, my dear young wife,
What have I done wrong?

Refrain:

Day-day-day, etc.

Would you have me tell you,
That I love you true -
Let us go upon a journey
To the ''pious Jew''.

He will bless us both,
A prayer he will say,
We will leave a token for him,
And go upon our way.

Un az mir veln kumen
Tsurik fun gutn yid,
Veln mir beyde ariberforn
In Zelva oyf dem yarid. (Ref.)

Dort vel ich dir koyfn
A zeyger mit a keyt,
Un a sheyne groyse shtik
Zaydns oyf a kleyd. (Ref.)

To, zay-zhe mer nisht broygez
Un greyt oyf gich tsum tish –
Un zets zich mit mir esn,
Bakumstu fun mir a kush! (Ref.)

On the journey homeward,
We'll drop in at the Fair,
Where I'll buy you pretty things
And presents very rare.

We'll get a bolt of satin
For a dress and train,
Then I'll also buy for you, my dear
A golden watch and chain.

So, don't be angry, dear wife,
Come sit beside me here,
Let us eat our meal together now,
Let me kiss you, dear.

Bulbes

Spuds

Poverty song. English text by Ruth Rubin, © 1964 by Appleseed Music, Inc.

Zun - tig bul - bes, Mon - tig bul - bes, Din - stig un Mit - voch __ bul - bes.
Spuds on Sun - day, Spuds on Mon - day, Tues - day and Wed - nes - day spuds.

Doner - shtig un Fray - tig __ bul - bes, O - ber Sha - bes in a no - vi - ne a
Thurs - day and Fri - day __ spuds. But the treat on the Sabbath is a

bul - be ki - ge - le Un Zun - tig vay - ter bul - bes.
pudding of po - ta - toes! And on Sun - day once a - gain, it is spuds!

Zuntig - bulbes,	Spuds on Sunday,
Montig - bulbes,	Spuds on Monday,
Dinstig un mitvoch - bulbes,	Tuesday and Wednesday - spuds!
Donershtig un fraytig - bulbes.	Thursday and Friday - spuds!
Ober shabes in a novine, a bulbe kigele!	But the treat on the Sabbath is a pudding of potatoes!
Un zuntig vayter, bulbes.	And on Sunday, once again, it is - spuds!
Broyt mit bulbes,	Its bread with spuds
Fleysh mit bulbes,	And meat with spuds,
Varimes un vetshere - bulbes,	Breakfast and dinner - spuds!
Ober un vider - bulbes.	Morning and evening - spuds!
Ober eynmol in a novine a bulbe kigele!	But the special dish is always the pudding of potatoes!
Un zuntig vayter bulbes!	And on Sunday, once again, it is spuds!
Ober - bulbes,	Now - its spuds
Vider - bulbes,	And later - spuds,
Ober un vider - bulbes,	Today and tomorrow - spuds!
Vider un ober - bulbes!	Week after week, it is spuds!
Ober shabes nochn tsholnt a bulbe kigele!	But the best on the Sabbath is the pudding of potatoes!
Un zuntig vayter, bulbes.	And on Sunday, once again, we get spuds!

Chatskele, Chatskele

Hey There, Chatskl

For those who are not at home in the Yiddish language, but who will want to sing the songs in the original, I would like to offer a bit of advice: Consult someone who knows the language and can transmit some of the subtleties of the song and its background to you. This is especially indicated in this type of song.

Wedding-dance song. English text by Ruth Rubin, ©1964 by Appleseed Music, Inc.

Chats - ke - le, Chats - ke - le, shpil mir a ka - zats - ke - le,
Hey, there, Chats - kl, Play it loud and bold ___ We

Chotsh an o - ri - me, A - bi a chvats - ke.
may be poor ___ but we've hearts of gold. ___

O - rim iz nit gut, O - rim iz nit gut,
Pov - er - ty's a curse, Pov - er - ty's a curse.

Lo - mir zich nit she - men mit ey - ge - ne blut.
Lets not shame our re - la - tives that have an emp - ty purse.

Chatskele, chatskele, shpil mir a kazat-
skele,
Chotsh an orime, abi a chvatske.

Refrain:

Orim iz nit gut,
Orim iz nit gut,
Lomir zich nit shemen
Mit eygene blut.

Nit kayn gebetene, aleyn gekumen,
Chotsh an orime, fort a mume.

Chatskele, chatskele, shpil mir a dume,
Chotsh an orime, abi a frume.

Hey there, Chatskl, play it loud and bold,
We may be poor, but we've hearts of
gold.

Refrain:

Poverty's a curse,
Poverty's a curse,
Lets not shame the relatives
That have an empty purse.

The wedding invitation came to us
belated,
We may be poor but we're still related.

Come now, Chatskl, play it loud and gay,
We are all Gods children on this wedding
day.

Dremlen Feygl Oyf Di Tsvaygn

Sleep My Baby, Hungry Baby

The shooting of 4,000 Jewish men, women and children at Ponar (outside of Vilna, Lithuania) on April 5, 1943, left a grievous impression on the young poet, who herself, soon after, perished at the hands of the Nazis. A three-year-old child, wandering in the streets after the roundup moved the poet to write this lullaby. The melody may have been adapted from a song by the Soviet composer Polonsky.

Yiddish text by Leah Rudnitsky, (1916-1943). English text by Ruth Rubin, © 1964 by Appleseed Music, Inc.

Drem-len fey-gl oyf di tsvay-gn, Shlof mayn tay - er kind.
Sleep my ba - by hun-gry ba - by, All the bir-dies are a-sleep

Bay dayn vi - gl oyf dayn na - re, Zitst a frem-de un zingt.
In the dug-out at your cra-dle A stran-ger soft-ly weeps.

Bay dayn vi - gl oyf dayn na - re, Zitst a frem-de un zingt.
In the dug-out at your cra-dle A stran-ger soft-ly weeps.

Lyu - lyu. Lyu - lyu. Lyu.
Lu - lu. Hush-a - bye. Lu.

Dremlen feygl oyf di tsvaygn,	Sleep my baby, hungry baby,
Shlof mayn tayer kind,	All the birdies are asleep.
Bay dayn vigl, oyf dayn nare,	In the dugout, at your cradle,
Zitst a fremde un zingt:	A stranger softly weeps.
Lyu-lyu, lyu-lyu, lyu.	Lu-lu, lu-lu, lu.
S'iz dayn vigl vu geshtanen,	You once had a home, my baby,
Oysgeflochtn fun glik.	A mother and father as well.
Un dayn mame, oy dayn mame,	Your mother was shot and died, in misery,
Kumt shoyn keynmol nit tsurik.	They stoned your father as he fell.
Lyu-lyu, lyu-lyu, lyu.	Lu-lu, lu-lu, lu.

Ch'ob gezen dayn tatn loyfn,
Unter hogl fun shteyn.
Iber felder iz gefloygn
Zayn faryosemter geveyn.
  Lyu-lyu, lyu-lyu, lyu.

Sleep my baby, hungry baby,
The moon is fast asleep.
In the dugout, at your cradle,
The stranger still softly weeps.
  Lu-lu, lu-lu, lu.

Du Meydele Du Fayns,
Du Meydele Du Sheyns

Pretty Little Girl, Can You Answer Me?

Riddle song. English text by Ruth Rubin, © 1964 by Appleseed Music, Inc.

Du mey-de-le du fayns, Du mey-de-le du sheyns, Ich
Pret-ty lit-tle girl   Can you ans-wer me?

vel dir e-pes fre-gn a re-te-nish a kleyns.
Do you know the ans-wers to my rid-dles one two three?

Vos iz he-cher fun ___ a hoyz? Un vos iz ___
What can grow ___ tal-ler than a house? And what is ___

flink-er fun ___ a moyz? Du na-ri-sher bo-cher du
swift-er than ___ a mouse? Sil-ly fel-low you,

na-ri-sher chlop! Host doch nit kayn sey-chl ___
You are stu-pid too, There's not a brain in-side your head, so

in ___ dayn ___ kop! Der roych iz he-cher fun ___ a
let me ans-wer you! Smoke ris-es tal-ler than a

hoyz, A kats iz flink-er fun ___ a moyz.
house, A cat is swift-er than ___ a mouse.

Du meydele du fayns, du meydele du sheyns,
Ich vel dir epes fregn, a retenish a kleyns:
-Vos iz hecher fun a hoyz?
Un vos iz flinker fun amoyz?

Du narisher bocher, du narisher chlop!
Host doch nit kayn seychl in dayn kop!
-Der roych iz hecher fun a hoyz,
A kats iz flinker fun a moyz.

Du meydele du fayns, du meydele du sheyns,
Ich vel dir epes fregn, a retenish a kleyns:
-Vos flit on fligl?
Un vos moyert on tsigl?

Du narisher bocher, du narisher chlop!
Host doch nit kayn seychl in dayn kop!
-Der shney flit on fligl,
Der frost moyert on tsigl.

Du meydele du fayns, du meydele du sheyns,
Ich vel dir epes fregn, a retenish a kleyns:
-Vos fara keyser iz on a land?
Un vos fara vasser iz on zamd?

Du narisher bocher, du narisher chlop!
Host doch nit kayn seychl in dayn kop!
-Der keyser fun kortn hot nit kayn land,
Trern fun di oygn zenen on zamd.

Pretty little girl, can you answer me?
Do you know the answers to my riddles, one, two, three?
-What can grow taller than a house?
And what is swifter than a mouse?

Silly fellow you, you are stupid too,
There's not a brain inside your head, so let me answer you:
-Smoke rises taller than a house,
A cat is swifter than a mouse.

Pretty little girl, can you answer me?
Do you know the answers to my riddles, one, two, three?
-What falls down and doesn't make a sound?
Builds without bricks upon the bare ground?

Silly fellow you, you are stupid too,
There's not a brain inside your head, so let me answer you:
-Snow when it falls, doesn't make a sound,
Frost needs no bricks to build upon the ground.

Pretty little girl, can you answer me?
Do you know the answers to my riddles, one, two, thre?
-Where is the king, without any land?
And where is there water without a grain of sand?

Silly fellow you, you are stupid too,
There's not a brain inside your head, so let me answer you:
-The king of hearts, he hasn't any land,
Tears from human eyes, haven't any sand.

Es Iz Gefloygn Di Gilderne Pave

The Golden Peacock Came A-Flying

In arranged marriages, the status of the groom's family rated higher, where the young husband was a scholar of the Torah. In these type songs, unhappy girls bewailed their fate, far from the tender love of parents, under the stern rule of a demanding mother-in-law.

English text by Ruth Rubin, © 1964 by Appleseed Music, Inc.

Es iz ge-floy - gn di gil-der-ne pa - ve,
The gol-den pea - cock came a - fly - ing,

I - ber a - le ya-men. Loz ge-ri - sn, du
A-cross the deep blue sea. Did my dear moth - er

gil-der-ner foy - gl, mayn li - ber har - tsi-ger ma - men.
send — you to me? Does she think of me? ___

Es iz gefloygn, di gilderne pave,
Iber ale yamen.
Loz gerisn, du gilderner foygl,
Mayn liber, hartsiger mamen.

Gefloygn, gefloygn, di gilderne pave,
Ibern taych dem glatn -
Loz gerisn, du gilderner foygl,
Mayn libn, hartsign tatn.

Gefloygn, gefloygn, di gilderne pave,
Iber ale felder,
Hot zi farloyrn dem gildernem feder,
In di fremde lender.

Nit azoy di gilderne feder,
Vi di pave aleyn,
Nit azoy der fremder zun,
Vi di tochter aleyn.

The golden peacock came a-flying
Across the deep blue sea.
Did my dear mother send you to me?
Does she think of me?

The golden peacock came a-flying
From across the wide water.
Fly, oh bird, and tell my father
Of his lonely daughter.

The golden peacock flew and flew,
Over fields so bare.
In a distant land she dropped her
Golden feather there.

A flying peacock is a thing of beauty,
A golden plume is but a feather.
A son-in-law is often a stranger,
But a daughter is yours forever.

Vi es iz bitter, mayn libe muter,
A vasser on a fish.
Azoy iz bitter, mayn libe muter,
Bay a fremdn tish.

Vi es iz bitter, mayn libe muter,
A feygele on a nest,
Azoy iz bitter, mayn libe muter,
Shver un shviger's kest.

Sad it is, oh dearest mother,
For a fish to be without water,
So it is at a stranger's table
For your unhappy daughter.

Sad it is, oh dearest mother,
When a bird is torn from its nest.
So it is in the house of in-laws
As an uninvited guest.

Eyder Ich Leyg Mich Shlofn

No Sooner to Bed

Work song, (Seamstress apprentice.) English text by
Ruth Rubin, © 1964 by Appleseed Music, Inc.

Ey-der ich leyg mich shlo-fn darf ich shoyn oyf-shteyn, Mit
No soon - er to bed, my bones full of pain.

may-ne kran-ke bey - ner tsu der ar - bet geyn. Tsu
Then I must rise to work ___ a - gain. To the

got vel ich vey - nen ___ mit a groys ge - veyn,
Lord I will weep, to the Lord I will cry.

vos ich bin ge - boy - rn a ney-to-rn tsu zayn,
Why was I born ___ a seam - stress, why?

Eyder ich leyg mich shlofn
Darf ich shoyn oyfshteyn.
Mit mayne kranke beyner
Tsu der arbet geyn.

Refrain:

Tsu got vel ich veynen
Mit a groys geveyn.
Vos ich bin geboyrn
A naytorn tsu zayn.

Ch'kum shpet tsu der arbet
S'iz doch vayt der veg,
Shlogt men mir op
Far halbe teg. (Ref.)

Di nodlen vern tsubrochn
Fuftsn a menut,
Di finger vern tsushtochn,
Es rint fun zey dos blut. (Ref.)

No sooner to bed,
My bones full of pain,
Then I must rise
To work again.

Refrain:

To the Lord I will weep,
To the Lord I will cry,
Why was I born
A seamstress, why?

Should I come late,
I live so far away,
I am docked
For a full half-day's pay. (Ref.)

The needles are old,
They constantly break.
My fingers, they bleed,
My God, how they ache! (Ref.)

Ich layd shtendig hunger
Ich hob nit vos tsu esn.
Vil ich gelt betn,
Heyst men mir fargesn. (Ref.)

The boss makes me wait,
When I ask for my pay.
I've nothing to eat,
I'm hungry all day. (Ref.)

IN COMPLIANCE WITH LAW?
The fire escape that ends in midair must be abolished.

Illustrations of the
Triangle Fire, N.Y.C., 1911
from the book "The Triangle
Fire", by Leon Stein,
published by J. B. Lippincott Co.

Eyn Kol, Eyn Kol, Eyn Kol Vayn

Sparkling, Bubbling, Lovely Wine

This song is an "unfinished" song and the "D.C. Al Fine" is there for each singer to add his own verses....

Drinking song, collected by Ruth Rubin. English text by Ruth Rubin, © 1964 by Appleseed Music, Inc.

Em
Eyn kol, eyn kol, eyn kol vayn. Eyn kol, eyn kol,
Spark - ling, bub - bling, love - ly wine, Spark-ling, bub - bling,

B7 Em Am
eyn kol vayn. Eyn kol, eyn kol, eyn kol vayn,
love - ly wine, Spark-ling, bub - bling, love - ly wine,

B7 Em *Fine* **Am Em**
Ich ken on dir nit zayn. Eyn kol vayn, Ich
You make me feel so fine. Fine, fine, fine, You

Am Em Am G Em
kon on dir nit zayn. Eyn kol vayn, —— Ich
make me feel so fine, Spark-ling, bub-bling, love-ly wine, You

B7 *D.C. al Fine* **Em**
kon on dir nit zayn.
make me feel so fine.

Eyn kol, eyn kol, eyn kol vayn, (3x)
Ch'ken on dir nit zayn.

Eyn kol, eyn kol, eyn kol bir (3x)
Ch'ken nit zayn on dir.

Eyn kol, eyn kol, eyn kol yash (3x)
Ch'vil a fule flash.

Eyn kol, eyn kol, eyn kol konyak (3x)
Ay, iz dos geshmak!

Eyn kol, eyn kol, eyn kol kvas (3x)
Ch'vil a fule fas.

Sparkling, bubbling, lovely wine (3x)
You make me feel so fine.
Fine, fine, fine, you make me feel so
    fine,
Sparkling, bubbling, lovely wine,
You make me feel so fine.

Gurgling, foaming, frothy beer, (3x)
You fill me full of cheer.
Cheer, cheer, cheer, you fill me full of
    cheer,
Gurgling, foaming, frothy beer
You fill me full of cheer.

Good old whiskey, strong and free (3x)
A bottle is right for me.
Right for me; a bottle is right for me,
Good old whiskey, strong and free
A bottle is right for me.

Cognac isn't bad at all (3x)
It makes me grow so tall.
Tall, tall, tall; it makes me grow so
    tall,
Cognac isn't bad at all,
It makes me grow so tall.

If only cider is around (3x)
I'll drink that barrel down.
Down, down, down,
I'll drink that barrel down,
If only cider is around
I'll drink that barrel down.

Gibn Dir Mayn Tochter

Tell Me, Darling Daughter

Conversation song. English text by Ruth Rubin, © 1964 by Appleseed Music, Inc.

Em
Gi-bn dir mayn toch-ter, Gi-bn dir mayn toch-ter, A
Tell me dar-ling daugh-ter, Tell me dar-ling daugh-ter, will you

Am B7 Em Am B7 Em
shus-ter far a man? A shus-ter far a man? A
be a cob-bler's wife? Will you be a cob-bler's wife? A

D G D G D
shus-ter far a man vil ich nit, A shus-ter's a toch-ter
cob-bler's wife I will not be, Patch-ing old shoes is

G D G D Em Am
bin ich nit, La-ten shti-vl kon ich nit.
not for me, My fa-ther was no cob-bler No, not he!

Refrain G B7 Em D G B7 Em D
Zits ich oyf a shteyn, Un kuk a-rop un veyn, Un
I sit here on a stone, And weep and wail and moan,

G D G D Em B7 Em
ze vi a-le mey-de-lech ho-bn cha-se-ne, Un, nor ich blayb a-leyn.
All the young girls are get-ting mar-ried, And I am left a-lone.

Gibn dir mayn tochter, gibn dir mayn tochter,
A shuster far a man? A shuster far a man?
-A shuster far a man, vil ich nit,
A shuster's a tochter, bin ich nit,
Laten shtivl kon ich nit.

Tell me darling daughter, tell me darling daughter,
Will you be a cobbler's wife? Will you be a cobbler's wife?
-A cobbler's wife I will not be,
Patching old shoes is not for me,
My father was no cobbler, no, not he!

Refrain:

Zits ich oyf a shteyn,
Un kuk arop un veyn,
Un ze vi ale meydelech hobn chasene
Un nor ich blayb aleyn.

Gibn dir mayn tochter, gibn dir mayn
    tochter,
A shnayder far a man? A shnayder far
    a man?
-A shnayder far a man, vil ich nit,
 A shnayder's a tochter bin ich nit,
 Neyen kleyder kon ich nit.

    (Ref.)

Gibn dir mayn tochter, gibn dir mayn
    tochter,
A lamdn far a man? A lamdn far a man?
-A lamdn far a man, vil ich yo!
 A lamdn's a tochter, bin ich yo!
 Toyre lernen, kon ich yo.

Final Refrain:

Zits ich oyfn dach,
Un kuk arop un lach,
Un ze vi ale meydelech hobn chasene
Un ich bin mit zey glaych!

Refrain:

I sit here on a stone,
And weep and wail and moan,
All the young girls are getting married,
But I am left alone.

Tell me darling daughter, tell me
    darling daughter,
Will you be a tailor's wife? Will you be
    a tailor's wife?
-A tailor's wife I will not be,
 Stitching and sewing are not for me,
 My father was no tailor, no, not he!
 (Ref.)

Tell me darling daughter, tell me
    darling daughter,
Will you be a scholar's wife? Will you
    be a scholar's wife?
-A scholar's wife I'll gladly be,
 Studying the Torah is right for me,
 My father was a scholar, that was he!

Final Refrain:

Upon the roof sit I,
Laughing merrily,
Now I have found my own true mate,
And all may envy me!

Hob Ich a Por Oksn

Have You Seen My Honey Bears?

In translating a nonsense song, what can one do, but substitute one type of nonsense for another? - and still manage to keep something of the atmosphere of the original song!

Nonsense-cumulative. English text by Ruth Rubin.
© 1964 by Appleseed Music, Inc.

Hob ich a por ok - sn, ok - sn, Vos zey bro-kn
Have you seen my hon-ey bears, hon-ey bears, Sit-ting up on

lok - shn, lok - shn, Ay — vun-der i - ber vun-der
wood-en chairs, wood-en chairs? Did you say, hon-ey bears,

vi di ok-sn bro-kn lok-shn. Dos iz mir a vun - der —
sit-ting up on wood-en chairs? Oh my dar-ling dear —

Dos iz mir a vun - der.
Does-n't it seem queer?

Hob ich a por oksn, oksn,
Vos zey brokn lokshn, lokshn,
Ay, vunder iber vunder,
Vi di oksn brokn lokshn,

Refrain:

Dos iz mir a vunder!
Dos iz mir a vunder!

Hob ich a por bern, bern,
Vos zey shtiber, kern, kern,
Ay, vunder iber vunder,
Vi di bern shtiber kern,
Un di oksn brokn lokshn, (Ref.)

Have you seen my honey-bears, honey-
bears,
Sitting up on wooden chairs,
wooden chairs?
Did you say: honey-bears
Sitting up on wooden chairs?

Refrain:

Oh my darling dear,
Doesn't it seem queer?

Hob ich a por tsign, tsign,
Vos zey kinder vign, vign,
Ay vunder iber vunder,
Vi di tsign kinder vign,
Un di bern shtiber kern,
Un di oksn brokn lokshn, (Ref.)

Hob ich a por hint, hint,
Vos zey machn tint, tint,
Ay vunder iber vunder,
Vi di hint machn tint,
Un di tsign kinder vign,
Un di bern shtiber kern,
Un di oksn brokn lokshn, (Ref.)

Hob ich a por hener, hener,
Vos zey klaybn shpener, shpener.
Ay vunder iber vunder,
Vi di hener klaybn shpener,
Un di hint machn tint,
Un di tsign kinder vign,
Un di bern shtiber kern,
Un di oksn brokn lokshn, (Ref.)

Have you seen my pussy-cats, pussy-
cats,
Dressed up in their fancy hats, fancy
hats?
Did you say: pussy-cats
Dressed up in their fancy hats?
Honey-bears on wooden chairs? (Ref.)

Have you seen my woolly sheep, woolly
sheep,
Rocking babies fast asleep, fast asleep,
Did you say: woolly sheep
Rocking babies fast asleep?
Pussy-cats in fancy hats,
Honey-bears on wooden chairs? (Ref.)

Have you seen my billy-goats, billy-
goats,
Sailing down on river-boats,
river-boats?
Did you say: billy-goats
Sailing down on river boats?
Woolly sheep fast asleep?
Pussy-cats in fancy hats?
Honey-bears on wooden chairs? (Ref.)

Hop, Mayne Homentashn!

Hey, Hey, Homentashn!

Purim song. English lyrics by Ruth Rubin, © 1964 by Appleseed Music, Inc.

Yach-ne Dvo-she fort in mark, Zi halt zich in eyn pa - kn,
I'll tell you of a pret-ty girl, Who was al-ways in a flur - ry,

Fort oyf Pu - rim koy - fn mel, Ho-men-ta-shn ba - kn.
She baked her Pu - rim ho-men-ta-shn, In an aw-ful hur - ry.

Hop, may-ne ho-men-ta-shn, Hop, may-ne vay - se.
Hey, Hey ho-men-ta-shn, You might have been so tas - ty,

Hop, mit may-ne ho-men-ta-shn Hot pa-sirt a may - se!
But you were the vic-tims of a pret-ty girl so has - ty!

Yachne-Dvoshe fort in mark,
Zi halt zich in eyn pakn,
Fort oyf purim koyfn mel,
Homntashn bakn.

Refrain:

Hop, mayne homntashn,
Hop, mayne vayse!
Hop, mit mayne homntashn
Hot pasirt a mayse!

S'geyt a regn, s'geyt ashney,
S'kapet fun di decher,
Yachne firt shoyn kornmel,
In a zak mit lecher.

I'll tell you of a pretty girl,
Who was always in a flurry,
She baked her Purim homentashn,
In an awful hurry.

Refrain:

Hey, hey, you homentashn,
You might have been so tasty-
But you were the victims of
A pretty girl so hasty!

That girl, she hurried off to town,
Shaking with her bustle,
To buy the flour and poppy-seed,
As fast as she could hustle.

Nit kayn honig, nit kayn mon,
Un fargesn heyvn,
Yachne macht shoyn homntashn,
S'bakt zich shoyn in oyvn.

Yachne firt shoyn shalach-mones,
Tsu der bobe yente,
Tsvey-dray homntashn,
Halb-roy, halb farbrente.

She forgot the salt, forgot the yeast,
It wasn't even funny -
The flour was in a sorry mess,
But her heart was sweet as honey.

Our maid then baked the homentashn,
But half were raw and pasty,
The other was burnt quite to a crisp,
The mess was far from tasty!

Hot Zich Mir Di Zip Tsezipt

My Old Sieve Was All Worn Out

About 20 years ago, when I first collected this Yiddish folksong from my Mother, she could not remember more than the first stanza! I was heartbroken. But in time, like most "carriers", I added two additional stanzas, which I sang and recorded time and again. But this is the first time I have confessed to having authored them!....

Dancing song. English text by Ruth Rubin, © 1964 by Appleseed Music, Inc.

Hot zich mir di zip tse-zipt un hot zich mir tsu-bro-chn,
My old sieve was all worn out, to-day it broke in two.

Hot zich mir di shich tse-ri-sn, tants ich in di hoy-le zo-kn.
Danc-ing in your stock-ing feet is bet-ter than in shoes.

Tants, tants ant-ke-gn mir, Un ich ant-ke-gn dir,
I will dance with you my dear, and you will dance with me,

Du vest nemen dem ey-dim, un ich vel nemen di shnir!
You can have the son in law, The daugh-ter-in-law's for me!

Hot zich mir di zip tsezipt
Un hot zich mir tsebrochn.
Hot zich mir di shich tserisn
Tants ich in di hoyle zokn!

Refrain:

Tants, tants antkegn mir,
Un ich antkegn dir -
Du vest nemen dem eydim
Un ich vel nemen di shnir!

My old sieve was all worn out,
Today it broke in two-
Dancing in your stocking-feet
Is better than in shoes!

Refrain:

I will dance with you, my dear,
And you will dance with me.
You can have the son-in-law,
The daughter-in-law's for me!

Tsebrochn iz der lokshntop,
Farbrent der nahit -
Tantsn di machteynestes,
Di kale in der mit.

Chosn's tsad un kale's tsad -
Di gantse mishpoche -
Tantsn oyf der chasene
In mazl un in broche!

Broken is my noodle-pot
The chickpeas burned inside.
All the ladies now are dancing
Round and round the bride.

Everybody's come to dance
And eat and drink right hearty,
Rich and poor and old and young
Have come to the wedding party!

Lomir Zich Iberbetn

Come, Let's Be Friends Again

Wedding dance folksong. English text by Ruth Rubin,
© 1964 by Appleseed Music, Inc.

Lo-mir zich i-ber-be-tn, i-ber-be-tn, Vos shtey-stu bay der
Come, lets be friends a-gain,— friends a-gain,— Don't stand there at the

tir? Vos shtey-stu bay der tir? Lo-mir zich i-ber-be-tn,
door. Don't stand there at the door. Come, lets be friends a-gain,—

kum a-rayn tsu mir. mir.
friends for ev-er-more. more.

Lomir zich iberbetn, iberbetn,
Vos shteystu bay der tir?
Lomir zich iberbetn,
Kum arayn tsu mir.

Come, lets be friends again, friends
    again,
Don't stand there at the door.
Come lets be friends again,
Friends for evermore.

Lomir zich iberbetn, iberbetn,
Vos shteystu bay mayn fenster?
Lomir zich iberbetn,
Bist bay mir der shenster.

Come, lets be friends again, friends
    again,
Don't hide behind the wall.
Come, lets be friends again,
I love you best of all.

Lomir zich iberbetn, iberbetn,
Koyf a por marantsn,
Lomir zich iberbetn,
Lomir geyen tantsn.

Come, lets be friends again, friends
    again,
We're birds of a feather.
Come, lets be friends again,
And dance about together.

Lomir zich iberbetn, iberbetn,
Shtel dem samovar,
Lomir zich iberbetn,
Zay-zhe nisht kayn nar.

Come, lets be friends again, friends
    again,
I'll put up the tea.
Come, lets be friends again,
Come and sit by me.

Lomir zich iberbetn, iberbetn,
Lomir nisht zayn vi geyrim,
Lomir zich iberbetn,
Lomir zayn chaverim

Come lets be friends again, friends
    again,
We will help each other,
Come lets be friends again,
I will be your brother.

Gey Ich Mir Shpatsirn

I Strolled Out One Spring Morning

Obviously of German origin. To keep the spirit of this saucy song, I have added an extra verse to the English translation.

Flirtation song, collected by Ruth Rubin. English text by Ruth Rubin. © 1964 by Appleseed Music, Inc.

Gey ich mir shpa-tsi-rn, Tra-la-la la la la.
I strolled out one Spring morn-ing, Fa-la-la la la la. I

Gey ich mir shpa-tsi-rn, Tra-la-la la la la la. Ba-
strolled out one Spring morn-ing, Fa-la-la la la la la. I

ge-gnt mich a bo-cher, a-ha! A-ha! Ba-ge-gnt mich a
met a fel-low court-ing, a-ha! A-ha! I met a fel-low

bo-cher, a-ha!
court-ing, a-ha!

Gey ich mir shpatsirn, tralala lalala.
Gey ich mir shpatsirn, tralala lalala, la.
Bagegnt mich a bocher, aha! (2)

Er zogt er vet mich nemen, tralala etc.
Er leygt es op oyf vinter, aha, aha.

Der vinter iz gekumen, etc.
Er hot mich nit genumen, etc.

Itst vil er mich shoyn nemen, etc.
Ober ich vil im nit kenen, aha, aha!

I strolled out one Spring morning, falala lalala,
I strolled out one Spring morning, falala, lalala, la.
I met a fellow courting, aha, aha! (2)

He said some day we'll marry, etc.
But now, he could not tarry, aha, aha!

The seasons passed me by, etc.
That fellow made me sigh, aha, aha!

Another fair Spring morning, etc.
That fellow came a-courting, aha, aha!

But all the while he tarried, etc.
Oh, I was safely married, aha, aha!

Mayn Yingele

My Little Son

This cradle song, of a sweatshop worker, was written in New York City in 1887, by Morris Rosenfeld. It was a time when the mass migrations of Jews from Eastern Europe were in full swing. Rosenfeld's poetry became very popular and a number of his poems were set to music by anonymous composers. His sung poems came to be known to Yiddish-speaking people on both sides of the Atlantic, and subsequently, wherever Yiddish was spoken. The two musical variants to Mayn Yingele given here, attest to this. Rosenfeld's poetry was also translated into English and then into a number of European languages (thanks to Leo Wiener, Professor of Literature at Harvard University at that time), which made him world renowned. Mayn Yingele too, has been translated many times, and into many tongues. Several English translations were made.

Text by Morris Rosenfeld, tune anonymous. English text by Ruth Rubin. ©1964 by Appleseed Music, Inc.

Ich hob a kley-nem yin-ge-le, A zu-ne-le gor fayn. Ven
I have a hand-some ba-by son, A lit-tle boy so fine. And

ich der-ze im dacht zich mir, Di gan-tse velt iz mayn. Nor
when I look at him I feel, The whole wide world is mine. But

zel-tn, zel-tn ze ich im, Mayn shey-nem ven er vacht. Ich
sel-dom do I see my child, When he's a-wake and bright. When

tref im i-mer shlof-n-dig, Ich ze im nor bay nacht.
I leave home he's fast a-sleep, When I re-turn its night.

Ich hob a kleynem yingele	I have a handsome baby son,
A zunele gor fayn.	A little boy, so fine.
Ven ich derze im, dacht zich mir,	And when I look at him, I feel
Di gantse velt iz mayn.	The whole wide world is mine.
Nor zeltn, zeltn, ze ich im,	But seldom do I see my child,
Mayn sheynem, ven er vacht.	When he's awake and bright,
Ich tref im imer shlofndig,	When I leave home, he's still asleep,
Ich ze im nor baynacht.	When I return, its night.
Di arbet traybt mich fri aroys,	To toil, I'm driven out at dawn,
Un lozt mich shpet tsurik.	Its dark when I return.
O fremd iz mir mayn eygn layb,	I seem a stranger to myself,
O, fremd, mayn kind's a blik.	Estranged from those I yearn.

Ich kum tsuklemterheyt aheym,
In finsternish gehilt,
Mayn bleyche froy dertseylt mir bald
Vi fayn dos kind zich shpilt.

When I come home so wearily,
My wife describes the day -
How happily our child does romp,
The bright things he does say.

Vi zis es redt, vi klug es fregt:
O Mame, gute Ma,
Ven kumt un brengt a pene mir,
Mayn guter, guter Pa?"

How wistfully he says to her:
Where can my Daddy be?
Will he come and bring some day
A penny, all for me?

Ich her es tsu, un yo, es muz,
Yo, yo, es muz geshen!
Di foter-libe flakert oyf,
Es muz mayn kind mich zen!

I listen sadly to her tale,
My wasted life I rue -
I want to see my child again!
For him to know me too...

Ich shtey bay zayn gelegerl,
Un ze un her un sha;
A troym bavegt di lipelech:
"O, vu iz, vu iz Pa"

I stand beside the little crib,
And watch my sleeping son.
In his dreams he's whispering;
Where has my Daddy gone?

Ich kush di bloye oygelech,
Zey efenen zich, O kind!
Zey ze-en mich, zey ze-en mich!
Un shlisn zich geshvind.

I gaze at him and kiss his eyes,
They seem to look at me!
But then they close, he's fast asleep-
Still whispering dreamily.

Do shteyt dayn Papa tayerer,
A penele dir, na!
A troym bavegt di lipelech;
O vu iz, vu iz Pa?

Your Daddy's brought your penny, son,
I kiss his tender brow.
The dream still whispers from his lips:
Where is my Daddy now?

Ich blayb tsuveytogt un tsuklemt,
Farbitert, un ich kler:
Ven du ervachst amol, mayn kind,
Gefinstu mich nit mer...

I look at him in anguish then,
I know - it seems so clear -
When once again, my child awakes -
His Daddy won't be here.....

Variant Melody

Ich hob a kley-nem yin-ge-le, A zu-ne-le gor fayn.___ Ven
I have a hand-some ba-by son. A lit-tle boy so fine.___ And

ich der-ze im dacht zich mir, Di gan-tse velt iz mayn.___ Nor
when I look at him I feel, the whole wide world is mine. ___ But

zel-tn, zel-tn ze ich im, Mayn shey-nem ven—er vacht.___ Ich
sel-dom do I see my child, when he's a-wake and bright. When

tref im i-mer shlof-n-dig, Ich ze im nor bay nacht.___
I leave home he's fast a-sleep, When I re-turn it's night.___

Michalku

Children's song. English text by Ruth Rubin, ©1964
by Appleseed Music, Inc.

G
Hob ich mir a kley-nem Mi-chal-ku, Mi-chal-ku,
I have a ver-y good friend Mi-chal-ku, Mi-chal-ku,

D
Voynt er oyf der lang - er gas. Macht er mir
He does-n't live so ver-y far a - way. He makes for me what-

G **D** **G** **D**
vos er ken Macht er mir vos er vil, Macht er mir a
ev-er I wish, he makes for me what-ev-er he can, Once he made a

G **D** **G**
pay - ke - le, Dos pay - ke-le macht a - zoy: Ta-ra -
lit-tle round drum, The lit-tle drum went ta-ra - boom! Ta-ra -

D
bam-bam- bam, Ta-ra - bam-bam - bam. A - zoy macht dos
boom-boom - boom, Ta-ra -boom-boom-boom, — Lis-ten to the lit-tle round

G
pay - ke - le.
drum.

Refrain:

Hob ich mir a kleynem Michalku,
 Michalku,
Voynt er oyf der langer gas.
Macht er mir vos er vil,
Macht er mir vos er ken:

Refrain:

I have a very good friend Michalku,
 Michalku,
He doesn't live so very far away.
He makes for me whatever I wish,
He makes for me whatever he can:

Macht er mir a paykele,
Dos paykele macht azoy:
Tarabambambam, Tarabambambam,
Azoy macht dos paykele! (Ref.)

Macht er mir a fayfele,
Dos fayfele macht azoy:
Flufluflu, flufluflu,
Azoy macht dos fayfele! (Ref.)

Macht er mir a fidele,
Dos fidele macht azoy:
Fidldidldidl, fidldidldidl,
Azoy macht dos fidele. (Ref.)

Macht er mir a trubetske,
Di trubetske macht azoy:
Trutrutru, trutrutru,
Azoy macht di trubetske. (Ref.)

Macht er mir a tsimbele,
Dos tsimbele macht azoy:
Tsimtsimtsim, tsimtsimtsim,
Azoy macht dos tsimbele. (Ref.)

Once he made a little round rum,
The little drum went: Taraboom!
Taraboomboomboom, Taraboomboom-
  boom,
Listen to the little round drum. (Ref.)

Then he made a whistle too,
This is how the whistle blew:
Fluflufluflu, flufluflu,
This is how the whistle blew! (Ref.)

One fine day he made for me,
the tiniest little fiddle-dee-dee,
Feedl-deedl-deedl, dee-dee-dee,
The nicest little fiddle for me! (Ref.)

He made a bugle for me too,
This is how the bugle blew:
Trutrutrutru, trutrutru,
This is how the bugle blew! (Ref.)

A triangle he made so small,
And said that that was really all.
It made a little tsimtsimtsim -
But that was absolutely all. (Ref.)

Ot Azoy Neyt A Shnayder

This Is How a Tailor Stitches

A work song of the beginning of the 19th century, acquires two additional stanzas (3 and 4), towards the end of the 80s, when the struggle for the ten hour day, was crowned with success, in a particular strike.

English text by Ruth Rubin, © 1964 by Appleseed Music, Inc.

Refrain:
Ot a-zoy neyt a shnay-der, Ot a-zoy neyt er doch.
This is how a tai-lor stitch-es, This is how he sews and sews.

Ot a-zoy neyt a shnay-der, Ot a zoy neyt er doch.
Mak-ing oth-er peo-ple's britch-es, All day long he sits and sews.

Er neyt un neyt a gant-se voch, far-dint a gil-dn mit a loch.
A tai-lor works hard all the time and all he gets is a lou-sy dime.

Refrain:

Ot azoy neyt a shnayder,
Ot azoy neyt er doch.
Ot azoy neyt a shnayder,
Ot azoy neyt er doch.

Er neyt un neyt a gantse voch,
Fardint a gildn mit a loch.

A shnayder neyt un neyt un neyt,
Fardint kadoches, nit kayn broyt.

Farayorn, nit haynt gedacht,
Hobn mir gehorevet fun acht biz acht.

Ober di struktsye hot gemacht,
Mir horeven shoyn mer nit fun acht biz
  acht.

Refrain:

This is how a tailor stitches,
This is how he sews and sews,
Making other people's britches,
All day long he sits and sews.

A tailor works hard all the time,
But all he gets is a lousy dime.

A tailor sews to earn his bread,
And gets the misery instead.

A year ago we worked till late,
Twelve long hours, from eight to eight.

But now the union's set us straight,
We work no more from eight to eight.

The tailor boss is in a fix,
We only work from eight to six.

Oyfn Barg Un Ibern Barg

Up the Hill and Over the Hill

English text by Ruth Rubin, © 1964 by Appleseed Music, Inc.

Oy - fn barg un — i - ber-n barg — fli - en toy - bn
Up the hill and — over the hill — ma - ting doves do

po - rn. Noch kayn na - ches nit der-lebt, shoyn a - vek di
fly. — Our young joys have come and gone, Life has passed us

1. yo - rn. **2.** yo - rn.
by. — by. —

Oyfn barg un ibern barg
Flien toybn porn.
Noch kayn naches nit derlebt,
Shoyn avek di yorn.

Lomir shpanen ferd un vogn,
Lomir loyfn, forn,
Efsher veln mir deryogn
Undzere yunge yorn.

Shoyn deryogt di yunge yorn
Oyfn hoychn brik.
Yorn, yorn, kert zich um,
Chotsh in gest tsurik!

Neyn, mir veln zich nit umkern,
S'iz nito tsu vemen!
Hot ir frier nit bedarft
Undz azoy farshemen!

Up the hill and over the hill
Mating doves do fly.
Our young joys have come and gone,
Life has passed us by.

Let us harness horse to wagon,
Let us quickly fly.
Let us overtake our youth
That has passed us by.

We caught up with our fair youth
At highbridge on the plain,
Return sweet years of long ago
Be our guests again!

No, no, no, we can't come back,
You're all old to-day.
You should not have, long ago,
Wasted us away...

Oy, A Nacht A Sheyne

The Moon Was Sailing in the Sky

Two lovers, faced with separation, decide to marry before he goes into the army.

English text by Ruth Rubin, © 1964 by Appleseed Music, Inc. (Last stanza collected by Ruth Rubin, 1964.)

Oy a nacht a shey-ne, __ Di nacht iz ge-ven a-zoy
The moon was sail-ing in the sky. __ The night was so soft and so

sheyn. __ Di sheyn. __ Af a ben-ke-le ze-nen mir ge-ze-sn, __ Di le-
blue. __ The blue. __ On a bench with our arms round each oth-er __ We

vo-ne hot ge-nu-men a-vek-geyn. ___ af a geyn.
sat there the whole __ night through. __ On a through.

Oy, a nacht a sheyne,
Di nacht iz geven azoy sheyn.
Oyf a benkele zenen mir gezesn,
Di levone hot genumen avekgeyn.

Oyf a benkele zenen mir gezesn,
Un hobn tsuzamen farbracht.
Vifil reyd mir hobn ayngetaynet,
Tsu kayn tolk hobn mir zich nit der-
   tracht.

Vos-zhe fara tolk libe, vilstu?
Az ich muz tsu dem priziv shteyn.
Kayn knasmol kenen mir nit machn,
Dos kenstu doch aleyn farshteyn.

Oyf banen vel ich forn,
Un oyf vasern shvimen tsu dir.
Ch'vel farlozn foter un muter,
Un kumen, zis-lebn tsu dir.

The moon was sailing in the sky
The night was so soft and so blue.
On a bench with our arms round each
   other,
We sat there the whole night through.

Oh, we talked for many long hours,
But what was there more we could say?
I had to go into the army,
I had to leave home the next day.

How can I marry you now, my dear,
Yet how can I leave you alone?
I know that you'll wait for me faithfully,
When in three years from now, I'll
   come home.

(She:)
I will ride the trains, oh my darling,
And sail over waters so blue.
I will leave both my father and mother,
Just to be, my own true love, with you.

Oyf kayn banen zolsu nit
  forn,
Un oyf vasern nit shvimen tsu
  mir.
A chupe, oy dushenyu, lomir
  shteln,
Un in dray yor vel ich kumen tsu dir!

(He:)
Don't you ride the trains, oh my darling,
And don't sail the waters so blue.
Tomorrow, I'll marry you, my own
  true love,
And in three years, I'll come back to
  you!

Oy, Dortn, Dortn, Ibern Vasserl

Away across the Hills

Love song. English lyrics by Ruth Rubin, ©1964 by Appleseed Music, Inc.

Oy, dor-tn, dor-tn i-bern vas-ser-l, Oy,
A-way a-cross the hills, and a-way a-cross the fields, A-

dor-tn, dor-tn, i-ber-n brik, _____ Far-
way a-cross the sea wide-and-blue, _____ I have

tri-bn hos-tu mich, in di vay-te-ne len-der, Un
gone and left you, love, in the land-of-me-mo-ry, And

ben-ken, benk ich noch dir tsu-rik.
sit here dream-ing now, my sweet, of you.

Oy, dortn, dortn, ibern vasserl,
Oy, dortn, dortn, ibern brik.
Fartribn hostu mich in di vaytene
   lender,
Un benken, benk ich noch dir tsurik.

Oy, vifil ovntlech, tsuzamen gezesn,
Oy, vifil ovntlech, shpet in der nacht.
Oy, vivil trerelech, mir hobn fargosn,
Oy, biz mir hobn di libe tsuzamenge-
   bracht.

Away across the hills and away across
   the fields,
Away across the sea, wide and blue.
I have gone and left you, love, in the land
   of memory,
And sit here dreaming, now, my sweet,
   of you.

I recall the gentle hours, the moonlit
   lovely hours,
When we promised all the love within
   our heart.
When we planned our life as one, for
   the happy years to come,
And now we're yearning, miles and
   miles apart.

Oy, dayne oygelech, vi di shvartse
  karshelech,
Un dayne lipelech vi rozeve
  papir.
Un dayne fingerlech, vi tint un vi
  feder,
Oy, shraybn zolstu ofte briv tsu
  mir.

I recall your eyes so black, like the
  cherries dark and ripe,
Your lips so pink, so soft and oh, so
  sweet.
I recall your slender hands and your
  fingers long and slim,
Oh Lord, I pray that once again we'll
  meet.

Oyfn Pripetshok

On the Little Hearth

This cradle song was written in the Czarist Pale of Settlement, where trials and tribulations were the natural environment of the Jewish Community. It was on the eve of the mass migrations to America and the lullaby actually anticipates the "exodus".

Mark Warshawsky authored more than fifty-texts and tunes, many of which were current among the people before they were published. Oyfn Pripetshok, however, became the most popular of his songs, and is known wherever Yiddish-speaking Jews reside the world over.

Text and Tune by Mark Warshawsky (1848-1907). English text by Ruth Rubin, ©1964 by Appleseed Music, Inc.

Oy - fn pri - pe - tshok   brent a fay - er - l,   Un   in shtub iz
On the lit - tle hearth, A fire is burn - ing bright, The school-room is so

heys.   Un - der re - be ler - nt   kley - ne kin - der - lech,
warm.   The old teach-er's tell - ing   all   the child-ren there, How the

1. Dem _ a - leph   beys.   2. Dem _ a - leph   beys.
al-pha-bet   was   born.   al-pha-bet   was   born.

Refrain

Zet-zhe kin - der - lech Ge-denkt-zhe tay - e - re,   Vos ir lern - t
Lis-ten chil - dren Lis - ten pre-cious ones, Lis - ten to   our

do.   Zogt-zhe noch a - mol un   ta - ke noch a - mol,
lore.   But first you have to read the   an-cient al - pha-bet,

1. Ko-mets a - leph,   O.   2. Ko-mets a - leph   O!
Be-fore you can   learn   more.   Be-fore you can learn   more.

Oyfn pripetshok brent a fayerl,
Un in shtub iz heys.
Un der rebe lernt kleyne kinderlech
Dem alef-beys.

Refrain:

Zet-zhe kinderlech, gedenkt-zhe
    tayere,
Vos ir lernt do;
Zogt-zhe noch amol, un take noch amol:
Komets-alef: O!

Lernt kinder, mit groys cheyshek,
Azoy zog ich aych on,
Ver s'vet gicher fun aych kenen ivre,
Der bakumt a fon. (Ref.)

Lernt kinder, hot nit moyre,
Yeder onhoyb iz shver,
Gliklech der vos hot gelernt toyre,
Tsi darf der mentsh noch mer? (Ref.)

Ir vet kinder, elter vern,
Vet ir aleyn farshteyn,
Vifil in di oysyes lign trern,
Un vifil geveyn. (Ref.)

Az ir vet kinder, dem goles shlepn,
Oysgemutshet zayn,
Zolt ir fun di oysyes koyech shepn,
Kukt in zey arayn! (Ref.)

On the little hearth a fire is burning
    bright,
The schoolroom is so warm -
The old teacher's telling all the children
    there,
How the alphabet was born.

Refrain:

Listen children, listen precious ones,
Listen to our lore,
But first you have to read the ancient
    alphabet
Before you can learn more.

It will lead you to the holy books,
Remember what I say -
Then I'll give a banner to the best of you,
On the holiday. (Ref.)

Pay attention, children listen well,
Its always hard to start -
Happy is the man who lives with knowl-
    edge,
Takes learning to his heart. (Ref.)

When you'll grow up into men some day,
Then you'll surely know,
How full of human tears is our old
    alphabet,
How full of trials and woe. (Ref.)

And if one day, we should be driven out
From this land of pain -
May you seek and find in our old alphabet
The strength to build again. (Ref.)

Papir Iz Doch Vays

One Day As I Was Walking

Love song. English lyrics by Ruth Rubin. © 1964 by Appleseed Music, Inc.

Pa - pir iz doch vays __ un tint __ iz doch shvarts. Tsu
One day as I was walk-ing __ down the bus - y street.

dir mayn zis le - bn, tsit __ doch mayn harts. Ich volt
Man-y pret - ty maid - ens I hap-pened to meet. But there

shten - dig ge - ze - sn dray teg __ noch - an - and, Tsu
wasn't __ one a - mong them that could at all com - pare, With my

ku-shn dayn sheyn __ po-nim un tsu hal - tn dayn hant.
true love's bright __ smile and her love - ly black hair.

Papir iz doch vays un tint iz doch shvarts,
Tsu dir mayn zis lebn, tsit doch mayn harts.
Ich volt shtendig gezesn, dray teg nochanand,
Tsu kushn dayn sheyn ponim un tsu haltn dayn hant.

Nechtn bin ich oyf a chasene geven,
Fil sheyne meydelech hob ich dort gezen.
Ay, fil sheyne meydelech, tsu dir kumt nit gor,
Mit dayne shvartse eygelech un mit dayne shvartse hor.

One day as I was walking down the busy street,
Many pretty maidens I happened to meet.
But there wasn't one among them that could at all compare,
With my true love's bright smile and her lovely black hair.

My darling is charming and gentle are her ways,
She has bound me with tenderness, forever and always.
My thoughts of her have filled me with purest delight,
I think of her all the day and I dream of her at night.

Ach du liber Got, her oys mayn
  farlang,
Dem oysher gistu kovid, mit a sheynem
  gang,
Oy, mir gib a shtibele oyf dem groz
  dem grinem,
Az ich mit mayn zis-lebn zoln voynen
  derinen.

On a hill in a mansion live the rich
  of our town,
They are laden with money, comfort
  and renown.
All I want is just one thing, it seems
  simple to me -
A little hut in the greenwood for my
  darling and me.

Shlof Mayn Kind, Mayn Treyst, Mayn Sheyner

Sleep My Baby, My Sweet Comfort

One of the most popular songs of the mass migration years of East European Jews to America, this lullaby was circulating among the people in Eastern Europe, in several textual and musical variants, even before it was published by Sholem Aleichem in Odessa, in 1892. Two versions are given here: the 1892 D. Kovanovski version and an anonymous version, transcribed by Ruth Rubin. Both are still current here.

Yiddish text by Sholem Aleichem. Melody based on a tune by D. Kovanovski. English Text by Ruth Rubin, © 1964 by Appleseed Music, Inc.

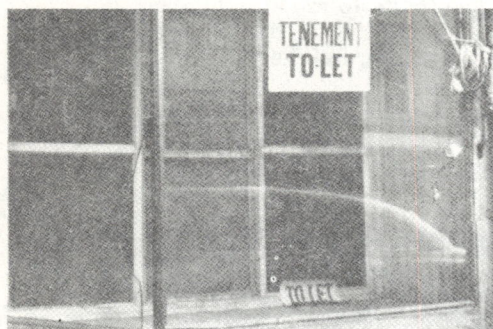

Shlof mayn kind, mayn treyst mayn shey-ner, Shlof-zhe zu-ne-nyu,
Sleep my ba-by, My sweet com-fort, Sleep my love-ly son.

Shlof mayn kind, mayn ka-dish ey-ner, Shlof-zhe, lyu, lyu,___ lyu.
Hush, my child, my pre-cious dar-ling, Hush, my lit-tle___ one.

Shlof mayn kind, mayn ka-dish ey-ner, Shlof-zhe lyu, lyu,___ lyu.
Hush, my child, my pre-cious dar-ling, Hush, my lit-tle___ one.

Shlof mayn kind, mayn treyst, mayn sheyner,
Shlof-zhe zunenyu,
Shlof mayn kind, mayn kadish eyner,
Shlof-zhe, lyu-lyu-lyu.

Bay dayn vigl zitst dayn mame,
Zingt a lid un veynt.
Vest amol farshteyn mistame,
Vos zi hot gemeynt.

In amerike iz der tate,
Dayner, zunenyu,
Du bizt noch a kind, lesate,
Shlof-zhe, lyu-lyu-lyu.

Sleep my baby, my sweet comfort,
Sleep my lovely son.
Hush my child, my precious darling,
Hush, my little one.

Mother sits beside your cradle
Crooning tearfully.
Some day, you will understand
What these tears mean to me.

Your daddy's in America
A thousand miles away,
You are still a tiny baby,
What more can I say?

In amerike iz far yedn,
Zogt men, gor a glik.
Un far yedn a gan-eydn,
Gor epes an antik.

America, the people tell me,
Brings good luck to all.
Everybody lives in comfort,
In houses very tall.

Dortn est men in der vochn,
Chale, zunenyu,
Yaychelech vel ich dir kochn,
Shlof-zhe, lyu-lyu-lyu.

In the weekdays, so they tell me,
They eat white bread, son,
Chicken broth, I'll make for you there,
Sleep now, little one.

Er vet shikn tsvantsig doler,
Zayn portret dertsu,
Un vet nemen, lebn zol er,
Undz ahintsutsu.

Twenty dollars and his picture,
Daddy'll send us here.
And we'll sail across the water,
To join him there, my dear.

Er vet chapn undz un kushn,
Tantsn azh far freyd,
Ich vel kvaln trern gisn,
Veynen shtilerheyt.

He will put his arms around us,
Kiss us joyfully.
I will be so happy, darling,
Weeping silently.

Biz es kumt dos gute kvitl,
Shlof-zhe zunenyu,
Shlofn iz a tayer mitl,
Shlof-zhe, lyu-lyu-lyu.

Till that blessed moment comes,
The days are sad and long.
Sleep is such a soothing comfort,
Sleep my son, grow strong.

Shlof Mayne Kind, Mayn Treyst, Mayn Sheyner
(version II)

Yiddish folk lullaby. English text by Ruth Rubin, ©1964
by Appleseed Music, Inc.

Shlof mayn kind mayn treys mayn shey - ner, Shlof mayn zu - ne - nyu,
Sleep my ba - by, my sweet com - fort, Sleep my love - ly son.

Shlof mayn kind, mayn ka - dish ey - ner, Shlof she lyu- lyu - lyu.
Hush my child, my pre - cious dar - ling, Hush, my lit - tle _ one.

Bay dayn vi - gl zitst dayn ma - me, Zingt a lid un _ veynt,
Moth-er sits be - side your cra - dle, Croon - ing tear - ful - ly,

Vest a - mol far-shteyn mis - ta - me, Vos zi hot _ ge-meynt.
Some day you will un - der-stand, _ What these tears mean_to me.

Shpilt-zhe Mir Dem Nayem Sher

Play That Lovely Tune for Me

A Sher is a traditional 19th century Jewish group dance.

English text by Ruth Rubin, © 1964 by Appleseed Music, Inc.

Refrain Em / Am / Em / Am / Em

Shpilt-zhe mir dem nay - em sher Vos iz a - roys - ge - ku - men,
Play that love-ly tune for me, The Sher that they're all danc-ing,

Am / Em / Am / Em *Fine*

Ich hob zich far-libt in a yin-ge-le a shey-nem, Un kon tsu im nit ku - men.
I'm in love with a hand-some lad, But I dare not go ro-manc-ing.

Em / Am / Em / B7 / Em

Ch'volt tsu im ge-ku - men, Voynt er zey - er vayt.
I would love to see him, But he lives far a - way.

G / C / D / G

Ch'volt doch im a kush ge-ge-bn, Shem ich zich far layt.
I would love to kiss him, But what would peo-ple say?

Em / G / Am

Nit a-zoy far layt, Vi far Gott a - leyn,
Its not so much the folks, But its the Lord I fear,

Em / B7 / Em *D.C. al Fine*

Ch'volt mit im far-bracht di tsayt az key-ner zol nit zen!
Oh, I would love to be with him, When no one else is near!

62

Refrain:

Shpilt-zhe mir dem nayem sher
Vos iz aroysgekumen,
Ich hob zich farlibt in a yingele a
    sheynem
Un kon tsu im nit kumen.

Ch'volt tsu im gekumen,
Voynt er zeyer vayt,
Ch'volt doch im a kush gegebn,
Shem ich zich far layt!
Nit azoy far layt,
Vi far Gott aleyn,
Ch'volt mit im farbracht di tsayt,
Az keyner zol nit zen! (Ref.)

Kum-zhe tsu mir gicher,
Ich vart oyf dir shoyn lang.
Kum-zhe gich ariber,
Men zol nit hern dayn gang.
Fir ich dich in shtibele,
Fun mayn mame'n aleyn,
Chosn-kale veln mir zayn
Un tsu der chupe geyn! (Ref.)

Refrain:

Play that lovely tune for me
The Sher that they're all dancing.
I'm in love with a handsome lad
But I dare not go romancing -

I would love to see him
But he lives far away.
I would love to kiss him -
But what will people say?
Its not so much the folks
But its the Lord I fear -
Oh, I would love to be with him
When no one else is near. (Ref.)

Come, my love, come softly,
Come quickly, I implore -
Let nobody see you, darling,
Coming to my door -
Come into my home -
And meet my family,
They will bless us both, my love,
And married we will be! (Ref.)

Shvartse Karshelech Raysn Mir

Red Cherries Are Not for Picking

Dancing song, Waltz. English text by Ruth Rubin,
©1964 by Appleseed Music, Inc.

Shvar - tse kar-she-lech ray-sn mir,— Roy - te lo - zn mir
Red cher-ries are not for pick - ing,— On-ly the black ones are

shteyn,— Shey - ne mey-de-lech ne-men mir,—
sweet,— We al-ways choose the pret-ty girls,— They are

Mi - se lo - zn mir geyn, Eyns-tsvey, eyns-tsvey-dray
nim - ble and fast on their feet, one - two, one - two - three,

Oy, vey iz tsu mir,— Vey iz tsu may - ne
Oh, woe is to me,— Woe is to me — I

yor, — A li - be hob ich ge - firt,— A
say, — I fell so deep-ly in love, — But the

fu - le dray-fer - tl yor.
sweet — thing got — a — way.

Shvartse karshelech raysn mir	Red cherries are not for picking,
Royte lozn mir shteyn.	Only the black ones are sweet.
Sheyne meydelech nemen mir,	We always choose the pretty girls -
Mi-se lozn mir geyn	They are nimble and fast on their feet -

Eyns tsvey, eyns tsvey dray -
Oy, vey iz tsu mir,
Vey iz tsu mayne yor -
A libe hob ich geshpilt
A fule dray-fertl yor.

Vos toygn mir di polke, mazurke,
Az tantsn, tants ich zey nit?
Vos toyg mir di sheyne figurke -
Az nemen, nemt zi mich nit - (Ref.)

Vos toygn mir di lipelech di sheyne
Az kushn, kushn zey mich nit?
Vos toygn mir di hentlech di kleyne
Az gletn, gletn zey mich nit - (Ref.)

Refrain:

One-two, one-two-three -
Oh, woe is to me,
Woe is to me, I say -
I fell so deeply in love -
But the sweet thing got away...

I cannot dance the Mazurka,
The Polka means nothing to me,
What's the use of my trying -
When the pretty girls won't have me!
(Ref.)

What good to me are her red lips?
I know they will never be kissing me -
What good to me are her little hands?
They'll not be caressing poor me. (Ref.)

Sheyn Bin Ich, Sheyn

I Am So Pretty

English text by Ruth Rubin,
© 1964 by Appleseed Music, Inc.

Sheyn, bin ich sheyn. Sheyn iz oych mayn no-men.
I am so pret-ty, Pret-ty's what they call me.

Redt men mir shi-du-chim mit groy-se ra-bo-nim. Ra-
Moth-er's look-ing for a rab-bi she wants me to mar-ry. The

bo-ni-she toy-re iz doch zey-er groys, —
wis-dom of the To-rah, is bet-ter far than mo-ney,

Bin ich bay mayn ma-men a lich-ti-ge royz.
Moth-er's ve-ry proud of me, her sweet ros-y ho-ney.

Refrain

A sheyn may-de-le bin ich, Bloy-e ze-ke-lech trog ich,
Pret-ty pret-ty that am I, I wear socks blue like the sky,

Gelt in di ta-shn, Bir in di fla-shn,
Wine in the brown jugs, Beer in the green mugs,

Vayn in di kri-ge-lech, Kind-er in di vi-ge-lech,
Mo-ney's ve-ry hard to keep, In the cra-dles ba-bies weep.

Shray-en vi di tsi-ge-lech: Meh, Meh, Meh. ____
Like the lit-tle wool-ly sheep: Maa, Maa, Maa. ____

Shlof Mayn Kind, Shlof Keseyder

Sleep My Baby, I Will Croon to You

English text by Ruth Rubin,
©1964 by Appleseed Music, Inc.

Shlof mayn kind, — Shlof ke-sey - der. Zing-en vel ich
Sleep my ba - by, *I will croon to you.* *I will sing you a*

dir a lid, Az du mayn kind ——— vest el-ter ve - rn,
lul-la-by When you, my child, grow up to be a man one day,

Ves-tu vi - sn an un-ter-shid. Az un-ter-shid.
You will know — the rea-sons why. *When rea-sons why.*

Shlof mayn kind, shlof keseyder,
Zingen vel ich dir a lid,
Az du, mayn kind, vest elter vern,
Vestu visn an untershid.

Az du, mayn kind, vest elter vern,
Vestu vern mit laytn glaych,
Demlt vestu gevoyre vern,
Vos heyst orim un vos heyst raych.

Di shenste palatsn, di faynste hayzer,
Dos alts macht der oriman,
Nor veystu ver es tut in zey voynen?
Gor nit er, nor der raycher man.

Der oriman, er voynt in keler,
Der vilgotsh rint im fun di vent.
Derfun bakumt er rematiz feler,
In di fis un in di hent.

Sleep my baby, I will croon to you,
I will sing you a lullaby,
When you my child grow up to be a man
    one day,
You will know the reasons why -

The reasons why our world's divided,
Why the poor man lives in pain,
Why he toils upon the land from dawn
    to dusk,
And the rich man reaps the grain.

The fancy mansions, the finest houses,
Stand so proud upon the hill,
But the man who builds, does not inhabit
    them,
No, not he, but the rich man will.

Poor men are sick and pale with
    overwork.
Wondering why they were born,
To live in cellars that are cold and
    damp and drear,
To starve and tremble in clothing torn.

Trink Bruder, Trink Oys!

Drink Brother, Drink Up!

Mordche Gebirtig was the most popular tunesmith in Poland between World War I and II. He was put to death in 1942, during the German-Nazi occupation. Author of more than a hundred texts and tunes, many of Gebirtig's songs (written in folk style) achieved the widest currency among Yiddish-speaking communities. "Reyzele", "Yankele", "Motele", "Dos Shtetele Brent", "Hey Tsigelech", are but a few examples of his "folksongs".

Yiddish text and tune by Mordche Gebirtig. English text by Ruth Rubin, ©1964 by Appleseed Music, Inc.

Trink bru-der, trink oys, Dos glez l biz tsum grunt. —
Drink, broth-er drink up! — *Down the hatch it goes.* —

Ves tu ve - rn — frish un mun - ter, Frey-lech un ge - zunt. Oy,
It helps us to for - get our trou-bles To bear our pain and — woes. Oh

bru-der - l le - chay-im, Trink a bi - se-le vayn,
Pro-sit broth-ers le - chay-im, Lets drink a bit of — wine,

1. Dos far-traybt di mo - re-sh'choy-re, ye - de zorg un payn. Oy,
That's what drives a - way the sor - row, Makes you feel so fine, Oh

2. Dos far-traybt di mo - re-sh'choy-re, ye - de zorg un — payn.
That's what drives a - way the sor-row, Makes you feel so — fine.

Trink bruder, trink oys,
Dos glezl biz tsum grunt.
Vestu vern frish un munter,
Freylech un gezunt.

Drink, brother, drink up!
Down the hatch it goes!
It helps us to forget our troubles,
To bear our pain and woes.

Refrain:

Oy, bruderl, lechayim,
Trink abisele vayn,
Dos fartraybt di more-sh'choyre,
Yede zorg un payn.

Itst bruder, trink ich,
Un vos felt mir atsind?
Ich fil zich gliklich vi a kenig,
Freylech vi a kind.

Itst bruder, trink ich,
Un ven es roysht in kop,
Fayf ich oyf der gantser velt
Un tants mir hop-hop-hop!

Refrain:

Oh Prosit, brothers, lechayim.*
Lets drink a bit of wine,
Thats what drives away the sorrow,
Makes you feel so fine!

When I drink up, boys,
I do not lack a thing,
I am happy as a youngster,
Mighty as a king.

When I keep drinking,
My head spins like a top,
I send my troubles to the devil,
And dance and skip and hop!

*Lechayim - the Jewish prosit. Literally it means
"To life".

New-York, May 20, 1766.

Joy to AMERICA !

At 3 this Day arrived here an Express from *Boston*
with the following most glorious News, on which
H. Gaine congratulates the Friends of *America.*
Boston, Friday 11 o'Clock, 16th May, 1766.
This Day arrived here the Brig *Harrison*, belong-
ing to *John Hancock*, Esq; Capt. *Shubael Coffin*,
in 6 Weeks and 2 Days from *London*, with the
following most agreeable Intelligence, *viz.*

Tsvey Taybelech

Two Little Doves

Love song. English text by Ruth Rubin,   © 1964 by Appleseed Music, Inc.

Tsvey tay - be-lech ze-nen   i - ber-n   vas-ser ge-floy - gn,
Two lit -tle doves_ were fly-ing a - cross _ the wa - ter,

Zey - e - re fli - ge - lech   ho-bn zey tsu-shpreyt.
Their wings out-spread _____   high up a - bove.

ho-bn zey tsu-shpreyt.   Far - shol - tn zol ve - rn   ye-ner
high up a - bove.   I   curse that per - son,   so —

mentsh oyf der velt, ___   Vos er hot undz in undzer li - be,   Oy _
wick - ed, so cruel, ___   Who came be - tween you and me,   my _

vey, tsu-sheydt.
own   true love.

Tsvey taybelech zenen ibern vasser geфloygn,
Zeyere fligelech hobn zey tsushpreyt.
Farsholtn zol vern yener mentsh oyf der velt,
Vos er hot undz in undzer libe, oy vey, tsusheydt.

Two little doves were flying across the wide water,
Their wings outspread high up above.
I curse that person, so wicked, so cruel
Who came between you and me, my own true love.

Un az du vest kumen in a vaytn land,
  lubelu,
In mayne verter zolstu zich badenken,
Un az du vest kumen iber a tifn vasser
  lubelu,
Far groys tsores zolstu zich nisht
  dertrenken.

Un az du vest kumen in a vaytn land,
  lubelu,
Mayne verter zolstu bakenen.
Un az du vest kumen iber a groysn
  fayer, lubelu,
Far groys tsores zolstu zich nisht
  farbrenen.

Tsvey taybelech zenen ibern vasser
  gefloygn,
In di piskelech hobn zey zich gekisht.
Farsholtn zol vern yener mentsh oyf der
  velt,
Vos er hot zich in undzer libe, oy,
  arayngemisht.

And when you will come to that strange
  city so far away,
Remember the warnings of my heart -
And when you will come upon a deep,
  wide water,
Don't drown your sorrow there, now that
  we're apart.

And when you will come to that strange
  land so far away,
Remember the words that I said.
And if you should come upon a fire
  that's burning,
Don't wish then, my own true love,
  that you were dead.

Two little doves were flying across the
  wide water,
Cooing and kissing above.
I curse that person so wicked, so cruel
Who came between you and me, my own
  true love.

Yeder Ruft Mich Ziamele

People Call Me Ziamele

Collected by Ruth Rubin. English text by Ruth Rubin,
©1964 by Appleseed Music, Inc.

Ye-der ruft mich Zia-me-le, Ay, vi mir iz shver.
Peo-ple call me Zia-me-le, I live all a - lone.

Ch'ob ge-hat a ma-me-le, Ch'ob zi shoyn nit mer.
Once I had a moth-er dear, But she's dead and gone.

Ch'ob ge-hat a ta-te-le, Hot er mich ge - hit,
I am beat-en like a dog, Be-cause I am a Jew,

Itst bin ich a shma-te-le, Vayl ich bin a yid.
Yet once I had the best of care, A good kind fa-ther too.

Yeder ruft mich Ziamele,	People call me Ziamele,
Ay, vi mir iz shver.	I live all alone.
Ch'ob gehat a mamele,	Once I had a mother dear,
Ch'ob zi shoyn nit mer.	But she's dead and gone.
Ch'ob gehat a tatele,	I am beaten like a dog,
Hot er mich gehit.	Because I am a Jew,
Itst bin ich a shmatele,	Yet once I had the best of care,
Vayl ich bin a yid.	A good, kind father too.
Ch'ob gehat a shvesterl,	I had a little sister then,
Iz zi mer nishto.	I don't know where she's gone.
Oy, vu biztu Esterl?	Oh, where are you Esterl?
In der shverer sho.	I'm scared to be alone.
Ergets ba a beymele,	Somewhere near a wooden fence,
Ergets ba a ployt.	On the ground so bare,
Ligt mayn bruder shloymele,	Lies my brother Shloymele,
Fun a daytsh getoyt.	A German shot him there.

Ch'ob gehat a heymele,
Itster iz mir shlecht.
Ch'bin vi a beheymele,
Vos der talyen shecht.
Ach du got in himele,
Kuk af der erd arop,
Ze nor vi dayn blimele,
Shnaydt der talyen op.

Once I had a cozy home,
Now on the ground I lie.
We are slaughtered just like sheep,
No one hears our cry.
Oh, dear God, look down on us,
And see our people slain.
The Germans butcher little ones,
There's no end to our pain.

Yomi, Yomi

Dancing song. English text by Ruth Rubin,   © 1964 by Appleseed Music, Inc.

Yo - mi, Yo - mi, zing mir a li - de - le Vos dos mey - de - le
Yo - mi, Yo - mi, why are you sigh - ing? Why are you sigh - ing my

vil? Dos mey - de - le vil a kley - de - le ho - bn,
dear? If a new dress is my Yo - mi's de - sire, ___ The

Darf men geyn der shnay - der - n zo - gn. Neyn, ma - me - shi,
fin - est seam - stress I will - hire. ___ No, moth - er dear,

neyn, Du veyst nit vos ich meyn, Du kenst mich nit far - shteyn.
no, My heart you do not know, A dress won't heal my woe.

Yomi, Yomi, zing mir a lidele
Vos dos meydele vil?
-Dos meydele vil a kleydele hobn,
Darf men geyn der shnaydern zogn -

Refrain:

Neyn, mameshi neyn,
Du veyst nit vos ich meyn,
Du kenst mich nit farshteyn.

Yomi, Yomi, zing mir a lidele
Vos dos meydele vil?
-Dos meydele vil a por shichelech hobn,
Darf men geyn dem shusterl zogn -
(Ref.)

Yomi Yomi...
Dos meydele vil a hitele hobn,
Darf men geyn der putserin zogn -
(Ref.)

Yomi, Yomi,...
-Dos meydele vil a por oyringlech
   hobn,
Darf men geyn dem goldshmid zogn -
(Ref.)

Yomi, Yomi,...
-Dos meydele vil a chosndl hobn,
Darf men geyn dem shadchendl zogn -

Final Refrain:

Yo, mameshi yo,
Du veyst shoyn vos ich meyn,
Du kenst mich shoyn farshteyn!

Yomi, Yomi, why are you crying,
Why are you sighing my dear?
-If a new dress is my Yomi's desire-
The finest seamstress I will hire-

Refrain:

No, mother dear, no,
My heart you do not know
A dress won't heal my woe.

Yomi, Yomi, why are you crying,
Why are you sighing my dear?
-If new shoes are my Yomi's desire,
The finest cobbler, I will hire -

Refrain:

(...Shoes won't heal my woe.)

Yomi, Yomi,...
-If a new hat is my Yomi's desire,
The finest milliner I will hire -

Refrain:

(...A hat won't heal my woe.)

Yomi, Yomi...
-If gold earrings are my Yomi's desire,
The finest goldsmith I will hire -

Refrain:

(...Earrings won't heal my woe.)

Yomi, Yomi,...
-If a bridegroom is my Yomi's desire-
The finest matchmaker I will hire -

Final Refrain:

Yes, mother dear, yes,
Now I must confess,
I want a husband, yes!

Yoshke Fort Avek

Yoshke's Going Off to War

This song originated in Vilna, Lithuania and is about an underworld character, "Yoshke", who preyed upon the small merchants in the Jewish quarter there. When the Russo–Japanese War broke out in 1904 and he was drafted, this satirical-humorous song describing an imaginary conversation between Yoshke and his lady-love, became popular. With the passage of time, however, folks began to interpret this song differently, with emphasis on the poignancy of separation in wartime. Both forms of interpretation are current.

Conversation song. English lyrics by Ruth Rubin, © 1964 by Appleseed Music, Inc.

Bak mir nit kayn bul - ke - lech, Ich vel zay doch nit e - sn,
Bake no hon - ey buns for me, for - get you ev - er met me,

Ich for a - vek fon - yen di - nen, Vest in mir far - ge - sn.
To the ar - my I must go, Oh, dar - ling don't for - get me!

Refrain

Oy, — Oy, — Oy, — Oy, — Yosh - ke fort a - vek.
Oh, — Oh, — Oh, — Oh, — In an hour or so,

Noch a sho un noch a sho der poy - ezd geyt a - vek.
Yosh - ke's go - ing off to war, to the ar - my he must go.

Bak mir nit kayn bulkelech,
Ich vel zey doch nit esn.
Ich for avek fonyen dinen,
Vest in mir fargesn!

Refrain:

Oy, oy, oy, oy,
Yoshke fort avek.
Noch a sho un noch a sho,
Der poyezd geyt avek.

(He:)
Bake no honey buns for me,
Forget you ever met me -
To the army I must go,
Oh darling don't forget me!

Refrain:

Oh, oh, oh, oh,
In an hour or so,
Yoshke's going off to war,
To the army he must go.

Koyf mir nit kayn lokenes,
Un mach mich nit sheyn.
Koyf dir a por shtivelech,
Tsum priziv darfstu geyn.

Refrain:

Oy, oy, oy, oy,
Yoshke fort avek.
Lomir zich gezegenen,
Der poyezd geyt avek.

Klog-zhe nit un veyn-zhe nit,
S'iz altsding blote!
Ich vel zayn bay fonyen,
Der shenster in der rote!

Refrain:

Oy, oy, oy, oy,
Yoshke fort avek.
Noch a kush un noch a kush,
Der poyezd`geyt avek.

Di ban iz shoyn gekumen
Un es chapt mich on a shrek!
Oy, vey, mamenyu,
Yoshke fort avek.

Refrain:

Oy, oy, oy, oy,
Yoshke fort avek
Lomir zich gezegenen,
Der poyezd geyt avek....

(She:)
Buy no pretty things for me,
What do I need them for?
Get yourself some army boots,
You're marching off to war -

Refrain:

Oh, oh, oh, oh,
My tears are flowing free,
Come back safely, my true love,
Oh, darling think of me!

(He:)
Don't you weep and don't you cry
The army's just a ball -
In the regiment I'll be,
The handsomest of all....

Refrain:

Oh, oh, oh, oh,
In an hour or so,
Come my darling, kiss me now,
The train's about to go...

(She:)
The train is moving out at last,
Oh, darling, how I grieve!
I cannot bear to see you go,
How can I see you leave?

Refrain:

Oh, oh, oh, oh,
Help me mother dear,
My true love has gone to war
For many a weary year.....

Zhamele

The sardonic tone of this song is evident.

Lullaby, melody anonymous. Yiddish text by A. Litwin (1862-1943). English text by Ruth Rubin, ©1964 by Appleseed Music, Inc.

Du vest zayn a g'vir mayn Zha - me - le,
"You'll be rich some day, my Zha - me - le,"

Fleg mir zing-en bay mayn vi - ge - le. A - le nacht a - mol mayn
At my cra-dle moth-er sang to me. Ev - ery night she'd croon the

ma - ma - le. Ich ge-denk noch haynt ir ni - ge - le.
same old song, I still sing her ten-der me - lo - dy.

Du vest zayn a g'vir, mayn Zhamele,
Fleg mir zingen bay mayn vigele,
Ale nacht amol, mayn mamele,
Ich gedenk noch haynt ir nigele.

"You'll be rich some day, my Zhamele",
At my cradle, mother sang to me.
Every night she'd croon the same old song,
I still sing her tender melody.

Un mekuyim iz gevorn mir,
Di havtoches fun mayn mamele,
Shver tsu gefinen aza groysn g'vir,
Aza'n oysher vi Zhamele.

At last, my mother's dreams have all come true,
Her fond wishes and great hopes for me—
I'm the wealthiest in all the land,
My riches are so plain for all to see...

shlofn, shloft er oyf a kerbele,
Macht hamoytse oyf a skorinke,
Un lechayim fun a sherbele
Trinkt er brunim-vasser klorinke.

I sleep each night without a single care,
On a bed of straw I lay my head,
I drink spring water from a broken shard,
Make my blessing on a crust of bread.

Un di kinderlech, dos vaybele,
Geyen oysgeputst antikele!
Ful mit lates iz dos laybele,
Arumgegartlt mit a shtrikele...

And my loving wife and family,
In rags and patches, in the latest style,
They're still singing mother's melody:
"You'll be rich some day, my darling child..."

Zits Ich Mir Oyfn Benkele

On a Stool, One Summer's Day

Teasing song. English text by Ruth Rubin, © 1964 by Appleseed Music, Inc.

Zits ich mir oyf-n ben-ke-le, Un far-kem mir may-ne
On a stool___ one sum-mer's day, Comb-ing my hair I heard a

he-re-lech, Geyt far-bay, oy, a shnay-der yung___
tai-lor say: She's a hus-sy but she's caught my eye___

Un zogt az ich bin nit er-lech!
So he teased me and made me sigh.

Zits ich mir oyfn benkele,
Un farkem mir mayne herelech,
Geyt farbay, oy, a shnayder-yung,
Un zogt az ich bin nit erlech.

Er zogt az s'iz tint,
Un ich zog az s'iz penes!
Er zogt az er hot mich lib -
Un ich zog az s'iz nit emes!

Zits ich mir oyfn fensterl,
Un farflecht mir mayne herelech,
Geyt farbay, oy, a shuster-yung,
Un zogt az ich bin nit erlech!

Er zogt az s'iz ash,
Un ich zog az s'iz koyln!
Er zogt az er vet mich nemen -
Un ich zog er vet nit poyln!

On a stool, one summer's day,
Combing my hair, I heard a tailor say:
She's a hussy but she's caught my eye -
So he teased me and made me sigh...

He said: ink is what you need my dear.
I said: no, its pens and that is clear!
He said: darling, I love but you -
I said: I don't believe you!

At my window, the other day,
Braiding my hair, I heard a cobbler say:
She's a hussy but she's caught my eye -
So he teased me and made me cry...

He said: ashes are very grey,
Burning coal is red-hot, I did say.
He said: darling will you marry me -
I said: Oho! we shall see!

Zhankoye

Dzhankoye was a depot in the Crimea, to which the Jewish collective farmers from the surrounding region would bring their produce. During the German occupation, the entire region was burnt to the ground.

Soviet-Yiddish folksong. English text by Ruth Rubin, © 1964 by Appleseed Music, Inc.

Az men fort kayn Se-vas-to-pl, Iz nit vayt fun Sim-fer-o-pl,
When you go to Se-vas-to-pol, Its not far from Sim-fer-o-pol,

Dor-tn iz a stan-tsi-ye far-an. Ver darf zuch-n
There's a de-pot in the sun. No need now to

nay-e glikn? S'iz a stan-tsi-ye an an-tik-l, In Zhan-koy-e,
be a rov-er All the fields here are in clo-ver, In Zhan-koy-e,

zhan, zhan, zhan. Hey! Zhan, Hey Zhan-koy-e,
zhan, zhan, zhan. Hey! Zhan, Hey Zhan-koy-e,

Hey Zhan-vi-li, Hey Zhan-koy-e, Hey Zhan-koy-e zhan, zhan,
Hey Zhan-vi-li, Hey Zhan-koy-e, Hey Zhan-koy-e zhan, zhan,

zhan. ——
zhan. ——

Az men fort kayn sevastopl,
Iz nit vayt fun simferopl,
Dortn iz a stantsiye faran.
Ver darf zuchn naye glikn?
S'iz a stantsiye an antikl!
In Zhankoye, zhan, zhan, zhan,

When you go to Sevastopol,
Its not far from Simferopol,
There's a depot in the sun.
No need now to be a rover,
All the fields here are in clover,
In Zhankoye, zhan, zhan, zhan.

Refrain:

Hey, zhan, hey, zhankoye,
Hey zhanvili, hey, zhankoye,
Hey, zhankoye, zhan, zhan, zhan.

Enfert yidn af mayn kashe,
Vu'z mayn bruder, vu'z abrashe,
S'geyt ba im der trakter vi a ban.
Di mume Leye ba der kosilke,
Beyle ba der molotilke,
In Zhankoye, zhan, zhan, zhan.

Ver zogt az yidn kenen nor handlen,
Esn fete yoych mit mandlen,
Nor nit zayn kayn arbetsman!
Dos konen zogn nor di sonim!
Yidn - shpayt zey on in ponim!
Tut a kuk oyf zhan, zhan, zhan.

Refrain:

Hey, zhan, hey, zhankoye,
Hey, zhanvili, hey, zhankoye,
Hey zhankoye, zhan, zhan, zhan.

Shout it brothers, you can bellow:
Abrasha is a handsome fellow!
He keeps that tractor on the run.
Bella's threshing, Leah's reaping,
There's no time for sighs and weeping,
In Zhankoye, zhan, zhan, zhan.

Some say Jews are only traders,
Can't work hard, are poor creators,
This slander's old beneath the sun.
For centuries for land we're thirsting,
Our silos now are full to bursting,
In Zhankoye, zhan, zhan, zhan.

Zog Nit Keynmol!

We Survive!

Hirsh Glik, poet of Vilna, was confined to the concentration camp Vayse Vake during the German occupation of World War II. In 1943, he joined the partisans and when the news of the Warsaw Ghetto uprising reached Vilna, he wrote this song. It immediately became the official hymn of the Jewish underground Partisan brigades. When the ghetto was liquidated, Glik was caught by the Gestapo and sent to a concentration camp in Esthonia. During the Red Army's offensive in the Baltic area, Glik escaped from the camp to the nearby woods, where he died fighting the Germans.

Text by Hirsh Glik (1920-1943). English text by Ruth Rubin, ©1964 by Appleseed Music, Inc.

Zog nit keyn-mol az du geyst dem lets-tn veg, Chotsh him-len
We must nev-er lose our cour-age in the fight, Though skies of

blay - e - ne far-shtel-n bloy - e teg. Ku - men
lead turn days of sun-shine in - to night. Be-cause the

vet noch un - dzer oys - ge-benk - te sho, S'vet a
hour for which we've yearned will yet ar - rive, And our

poyk ton un - dzer trot, mir ze - nen do! Ku - men
march - ing steps will thun - der: We sur - vive! Be-cause the

vet noch un - dzer oys - ge-benk - te sho, S'vet a
hour for which we've yearned will yet ar - rive, And our

poyk ton undz - er trot, mir ze - nen do!
march - ing steps will thun der: We sur - vive!

Zog nit keynmol az du geyst dem letstn veg,
Chotsh himlen blayene farshteln bloye teg,
Kumen vet noch undzer oysgebenkte sho,
S'vet a poyk ton undzer trot - mir zenen do!

Fun grinem palmen-land biz vaytn land fun shney,
Mir kumen on mit undzer payn, mit undzer vey,
Un vu gefaln s'iz a shprits fun undzer blut,
Shprotsn vet dort undzer gvure, undzer mut.

S'vet di morgn-zun bagildn undz dem haynt,
Un der nechtn vet farshvindn mitn faynt,
Nor oyb farzamen vet di zun un der kayor -
Vi a parol zol geyn dos lid fun dor tsu dor.

Dos lid geshribn iz mit blut un nit mit blay,
S'iz nit kayn lidl fun a foygl oyf der fray,
Dos hot a folk tsvishn falndike vent,
Dos lid gezungen mit naganes in di hent.

To zog nit keynmol az du geyst dem letstn veg,
Chotsh himlen blayene farshteln bloye teg,
Kumen vet noch undzer oysgebenkte sho,
S'vet a poyk ton undzer trot - mir zenen do!

We must never lose our courage in the fight,
Though skies of lead turn days of sunshine into night.
Because the hour for which we've yearned will yet arrive,
And our marching steps will thunder: we survive!

From land of palm trees to the land of distant snow,
We have come with our deep sorrow and our woe,
And everywhere our blood was innocently shed,
Our fighting spirits will again avenge our dead.

The golden rays of morning sun will dry our tears,
Dispelling bitter agony of yesteryears,
But if the sun and dawn with us will be delayed-
Then let this song ring out the call to you, instead.

Not lead, but blood inscribed this song which now we sing,
Its not a caroling of birds upon the wing,
But a people midst the crashing fires of hell,
Sang this song and fought courageous till it fell!

So we must never lose our courage in the fight,
Though skies of lead turn days of sunshine into night.
Because the hour for which we've yearned will yet arrive,
And our marching steps will thunder: We survive!

Zolst Azoy Lebn Un Zayn Gezint

I'll Sing to the Baby and It Won't Cry

This baby-sitter is a little girl of no more than ten years old....

English text by Ruth Rubin, ©1964 by Appleseed Music, Inc. (Last stanza collected by Ruth Rubin.)

Zolst a-zoy le-bn un zayn ge-zint, Vi ich — vel dir zit-sn un
I'll sing to your ba - by, It won't cry, I'll wait till you come home —

vi-gn dos kind. Ay - lyu - lyu, Sha - sha - sha, Di
by and by. Hush, lit-tle ba - by, Don't you cry, Your

ma - me iz ge - gang-en in mark a-rayn. Ay - lyu - lyu,
mom-my will come home — by and by. Sleep lit-tle ba - by, I'll

Shlof mayn kind, Di ma - me-shi vet ku - men gich un gesh-vind.
sing you a song, Your mom-my will come home, she won't be long.

Zolst azoy lebn un zayn gezint,
Vi ich vel dir zitsn un vign dos kind.

Refrain:
Ay-lyu-lyu, sha-sha-sha
Di mame iz gegangen in mark arayn.
Ay-lyu-lyu, shlof mayn kind,
Di mameshi vet kumen gich un geshvind.

Andere meydelech tantsn un shpringen,
Un ich darf dem kind lidelech zingen.
(Ref.)

Andere meydelech tsukerkelech nashn,
Un ich darf dem kind's vindelech vashn.
(Ref.)

Dayn mame iz a tshatshke aza yor af ir,
Az du shlofst nit ayn, shrayt zi af mir.
(Ref.)

I'll sing to your baby, it won't cry,
I'll wait till you come home, by and by.

Refrain:
Hush little baby, don't you cry,
Your mommy will come home by and by.
Sleep little baby, I'll sing you a song,
Your mommy will return, she won't be long.

Other little girls can romp and play,
But I must sing to baby all the day.

While other little girls eat sugar candies,
Your mother makes me scrub your dirty panties...

Your mother's a mean one, this I know,
If you don't go to sleep, she'll scold me so!

Vacht Oyf!

Awake!

Prominent labor poet of the 80's and 90's in the U.S.A., fourteen of Edelshtat's poems are known to have been set to music by anonymous composers, and widely sung by Jewish workingmen on both sides of the Atlantic.

Yiddish text by David Edelshtat (1866-1892), tune anonymous. English text by Ruth Rubin, ©1964 by Appleseed Music, Inc.

Vi lang, o vi lang vet ir blay - bn noch shkla - fn, un
How long, oh how long will you suf - fer in bond - age, in

tro - gn di shend - le - che keyt? Vi lang vet ir glents - n - de
sla - ver - y still to re - main? How long will you toil to cre -

raych - ti - mer sha - fn far dem vos ba - roybt - ay - er broyt? Vi broyt?
ate all the ri - ches for those who re - ward you with pain? How pain?

Vi lang, o vi lang vet ir blaybn noch shklafn
Un trogn di shendleche keyt?
Vi lang vet ir glentsende raychtimer shafn
For dem, vos baroybt ayer broyt?

Vi lang vet ir shteyn, ayer rukn geboygn,
Derniderikt, heymloz, farshmacht?
Es togt shoyn! vacht oyf un tsu-efnt di oygn!
Derfilt ayer ayzerne macht!

Klingt umetum in di frayhayts-glokn!
Farzamlt di laydende knecht!
Un kemft bagaystert, un kemft umder-shrokn,
Far ayere heylike recht!

Un ales vet lebn, un libn, un bli-en,
In frayen, in goldenem may!
Brider! genug far tiranen tsu kni-en,
Shvert, az ir muzt vern fray!

How long, oh how long will you suffer in bondage
In slavery still to remain?
How long will you toil to create all the riches
For those, who reward you with pain?

How long, oh how long will you carry the yoke
Of oppression and sorrow and fear?
Awaken! and see the new day that is dawning,
A free song is ringing mighty clear!

Ring out, bells of freedom, lets gather together
The suffering slaves in all lands,
Lets struggle for life and for love and for beauty,
Created by hardy toiling hands.

(P. 80) **זשאַנקױע**

אז מען פֿאָרט קײן סעװאַסטאָפּאָל,
איז ניט װײַט פֿון סימפֿעראָפּאָל,
דאָרטן איז אַ סטאַנציע פֿאַראַן.
װער דאַרף זוכן נײע גליקן?
ס'איז אַ סטאַנציע, אין אַנטיקל!
אין זשאַנקױע, זשאַן, זשאַן.

צוזינג:
הײ זשאַן, הײ זשאַנקױע,
הײ זשאַנװילי, הײ זשאַנקױע,
הײ זשאַנקױע, זשאַן, זשאַן.

ענטפֿערס אידן אױף מײן קשיא,
װאו'ז מײן ברודער, װאו'ז אבראשע?
ס'גײט בײ אים דער טראַקטאָר װי אַ באַן.
די מומע לאה בײ דער קאָסילקע,
בײלע בײ דער מאָלאַסילקע,
אין זשאַנקױע, זשאַן, זשאַן.

װער זאָגט אַז אידן קענען נאָר האַנדלען,
עסן פֿעטס יױך מיט מאַנדלען,
נאָר ניט זײן קײן אַרבעטסמאַן?
דאָס קאַנען זאָגן נאָר די שׂונאים,
אידן שפּײט זײ אָן אין פּנים!
טוט אַ קוק אױף זשאַן, זשאַן, זשאַן.

(P. 79) **זיץ איך מיר אױפֿן בענקעלע**

זיץ איך מיר אױפֿן בענקעלע,
און פֿאַרקעם מיר מײנע האָרעלעך,
גײט פֿאַרבײ, אױ, אַ שנײדער-יונג,
און זאָגט אַז איך בין ניט ערליך.

ער זאָגט אַז ס'איז זינס,
און איך זאָג אַז ס'איז פֿענעס!
ער זאָגט אַז ער האָט מיך ליב,
און איך זאָג אַז ס'איז ניט אמת!

זיץ איך מיר אױפֿן פֿענסטערל,
און פֿאַרפֿלעכט מיר מײנע האָרעלעך,
גײט פֿאַרבײ, אױ, אַ ?וסטער-יונג,
און זאָגט אַז איך בין ניט ערליך!

ער זאָגט אַז ס'איז אַש,
און איך זאָג אַז ס'איז קױלן!
ער זאָגט אַז ער האָט מיך געמען,
און איך זאָג ער האָט ניט פֿױלן!

(P. 82) **זאָג ניט קײנמאָל**

זאָג ניט קײנמאָל אז דו גײסט דעם לעצטן װעג,
כאָטש הימלען בלײענע פֿאַרשטעלן בלױע טעג,
קומען װעט נאָך אונדזער אױסגעבענקטע שעה,
ס'װעט אַ פּױק טאָן אונדזער טראָט – מיר זײנען דאָ!

פֿון גרינעם פֿאַלמען-לאַנד ביז װײסן לאַנד פֿון שנײ,
מיר קומען אָן מיט אונדזער פֿײן, מיט אונדזער װײ,

און װאו געפֿאַלן ס'איז אַ שפּראַץ פֿון אונדזער בלוט,
שפּראַצן װעט דאָרט אונדזער גבֿורה, אונדזער מוט.

ס'װעט די מאָרגן-זון באַגילדן אונדז דעם הײנט,
און דער נעכטן װעט פֿאַרשװינדן מיטן פֿײַנט,
נאָר אױב פֿאַרזאַמען װעט די זון אין דער קאַיאָר,
װי אַ פּאַראָל זאָל גײן דאָס ליד פֿון דור צו דור.

דאָס ליד געשריבן איז מיט בלוט און ניט מיט בלײ,
ס'איז ניט קײן לידל פֿון אַ פֿױגל אױף דער פֿרײ,
דאָס האָט אַ פֿאָלק צװישן פֿאַלנדיקע װענט,
דאָס ליד געזונגען מיט נאַגאַנעס אין די הענט.

טאָ, זאָג ניט קײנמאָל אז דו גײסט דעם לעצטן װעג,
כאָטש הימלען בלײענע פֿאַרשטעלן בלױע טעג,
קומען װעט נאָך אונדזער אױסגעבענקטע שעה,
ס'װעט אַ פּױק טאָן אונדזער טראָט – מיר זײַנען דאָ!

(P. 84) **זאָלסט אזױ לעבן און זײַן געזונט**

זאָלסט אזױ לעבן און זײַן געזונט,
װי איך װעל דיר זיצן און װיגן דאָס קינד.

צוזינג:
אי ליו ליו, שאַ-שאַ-שאַ,
די מאַמע איז געגאַנגען אין מאַרק אַרײן.
אי ליו ליו, שלאָף מײַן קינד,
די מאַמעשי װעט קומען גיך און געשװינד.

אנדערע מײדעלעך טאַנצן און שפּרינגען,
און איך דאַרף דאָס קינד לידעלעך זינגען.

אנדערע מײדעלעך צוקערקעלעך נאַשן,
און איך דאַרף דעם קינד'ס װינדעלעך װאַשן.

דײַן מאַמע איז אַ סטאַטשקע, אזױ יאָר אַף איר,
אז דו שלאָפֿסט ניט אײן, שרײַס זי אױף מיר.

זרקא   סגל מונח רביע

מהפך פשטא זקף זקף דרגא תביר
קטן גדול

יאַשקע פֿאָרט אַוועק (P. 76)

באַק מיר ניט קײן בולקעלעך,
איך וועל זיי דאָך ניט עסן,
איך פֿאָר אַוועק פֿאַניען דינען,
וועסט אין מיר פֿאַרגעסן.

אוי, אוי, אוי, אוי,
יאַשקע פֿאָרט אַוועק.
נאָך אַ שעה און נאָך אַ שעה,
דער פֿאַיעזד גייט אַוועק.

קויף מיר ניט קײן לאָקשעלן,
און מאַך מיך ניט זײן,
קויף דיר אַ פֿאַר שטיוועלעך,
צום פֿריזיע דאָרפּסט גיין.

אוי, אוי, אוי, אוי,
יאַשקע פֿאָרט אַוועק.
לאָמיר זיך געזעגענען,
דער פֿאַיעזד גייט אַוועק.

קלאָג-זשע ניט און ווין-זשע ניט,
ס'איז אַלצדינג בלאָס!
איך וועל זײן בײ פֿאַניען'ן,
דער שענסטער אין דער ראָט!

אוי, אוי, אוי, אוי,
יאַשקע פֿאָרט אַוועק.
נאָך אַ קוש און נאָך אַ קוש,
דער פֿאַיעזד גייט אַוועק.

די באַן איז שוין געקומען
און עס כאַפּט מיך אָן אַ שרעק!
אוי, ווי, מאַמעניו,
יאַשקע פֿאָרט אַוועק.

אוי, אוי, אוי, אוי,
יאַשקע פֿאָרט אַוועק.
לאָמיר זיך געזעגענען,
דער פֿאַיעזד גייט אַוועק...

זשאַמעלע (P. 78)

דו וועסט זײן אַ גביר, מײן זשאַמעלע,
פֿלעג מיר זינגען בי מײן חיגעלע,
אַלע נאַכט אַמאָל, מײן מאַמעלע,
איך געדענק נאָך הינט איר ניגעלע.

און סקוים איז געחאַרן מיר,
די הבטחות פֿון מײן מאַמעלע,
שוער צו געפֿינען אַזאַ גרויסן גביר,
אַזאַ'ן עושר ווי זשאַמעלע.

סלאָפֿן, סלאָפּט ער אויף אַ פֿערבעלע,
מאַכט המוצאַי אויף אַ סקאַרינקע,
און לחיים פֿון אַ שערבעלע,
טרינקט ער בראָנים-חאַסער קלאָרינקע.

און די קינדערלעך, דאָס חירבעלע,
גייען אויסגעפוצט אַנטיקעלע,
פֿול מיט לאַסעס איז דאָס ליבעלע,
א'וסגענאָרסלס מיט אַ שטריקעלע...

יעדער רופֿט מיך זיאַמעלע (P. 72)

יעדער רופֿט מיך זיאַמעלע,
אַי, ווי מיר איז שוער.
כ'האָב געהאַט אַ מאַמעלע,
כ'האָב זי שוין ניט מער.
כ'האָב געהאַט אַ טאַטעלע,
האָט ער מיך געהיס.
איצט בין איך אַ שמאַטעלע,
ווײל איך בין אַ איד.

כ'האָב געהאַט אַ שוועסטערל,
איז זי מער נישטאָ,
אוי, וואו ביזטו אסתרל,
אין דער שוערער שעה?
ערגעץ בײ אַ ברימעלע,
ערגעץ בײ אַ פֿליס,
ליגט מײן ברודער שלמהלע,
פֿון אַ דריש געטויס.

כ'האָב געהאַט אַ היימעלע,
איצט איז מיר סלעכט.
כ'בין ווי אַ בהמהלע,
וואָס דער תליון שעכט.
אָך דו גאַט אין הימעלע,
קוק אויף דער ערד אַראָפּ,
זע נאָר ווי דײן בלימעלע,
שנײַדט דער תליון אָפּ.

יאַמי, יאַמי, זינג מיר אַ לידעלע (P. 74)

יאַמי, יאַמי, זינג מיר אַ לידעלע,
וואָס דאָס מידעלע וויל?
– דאָס מידעלע וויל אַ קלײדעלע האָבן,
דאַרף מען גיין דער שנײַדערין זאָגן –

<u>צוזינג:</u>
ניין, מאַמעשי ניין,
דו חיסט ניט חאָס איך מײן,
דו קענסט מיך ניט פֿארסטיין.

יאַמי, יאַמי, זינג מיר אַ לידעלע,
וואָס דאָס מידעלע וויל?
– דאָס מידעלע וויל אַ פֿאַר שיכעלעך
האָבן,
דאַרף מען גיין דעם שוסטערל זאָגן –

<u>צוזינג:</u>
– דאָס מידעלע וויל אַ היסעלע האָבן,
דאַרף מען גיין דער פוצערין זאָגן –

<u>צוזינג:</u>
דאָס מידעלע וויל אַ פֿאַר אוירינגלעך
האָבן,
דאַרף מען גיין דעם גאָלדשמיד זאָגן –

<u>צוזינג:</u>
דאָס מידעלע וויל אַ חתנדל האָבן,
דאַרף מען גיין דעם שדכנדל זאָגן –

<u>צוזינג:</u>
יאָ, מאַמעשי יאָ,
דו חיסט שוין חאָס איך מײן,
דו קענסט מיך שוין פֿארסטיין!

(P. 62) שפּילט-זשע מיר דעם נײעם שער

צוזינג:
שפּילט-זשע מיר דעם נײעם שער
װאָס איז אַרויסגעקומען,
איך האָב זיך פֿאַרליבט אין אַן אײנגעלע
אַ שײנעם,
און קאָן צו אים ניס קומען.

כ'װאָלט צו אים געקומען,
װאוינט ער זייער װײט,
כ'װאָלט דאָך אַ קוס געגעבן,
שעם איך זיך פֿאַר לײט.
ניט אַזוי פֿאַר לײט,
חי פֿאַר גאָט אַלײן,
כ'װאָלט מיט אים פֿאַרבראַכט די צײט
אַז קינדער זאָל ניט זען.

קום-זשע צו מיר גיכער,
איך װאַרט אויף דיר שוין לאַנג.
קום-זשע גין אריבער,
מען זאָל ניס הערן דרן גאַנג.
פֿיר איך דיך אין שטיבעלע
פֿון מײן מאַמען אַלײן,
חתן-כּלה װעלן מיר זײן
און צו דער חופּה גײן!

שװאַרצע קאַרשעלעך רײסן מיר (P. 64)

שװאַרצע קאַרשעלעך רײסן מיר,
רויסע לאָזן מיר שטײן.
שײנע מײדעלעך נעמען מיר,
מיאוסע לאָזן מיר גײן.

צוזינג:
אײנס-צװײ, אײנס-צװײ-דרײ –
אוי, װײ איז צו מיר,
חי איז צו מײנע יאָר –
אַ ליבע האָב איך געשפּילט
אַ פֿולע דרײַ-פֿערטל יאָר.

וואָס טויג מיר די פֿאַלקעפּ, מאַזורקעפּ,
אַז סאאנצן, סאַנק איך זײ ניס?
וואָס טויג מיר די שײנע פֿיגורקעפּ,
אַז נעמען, נעמט זי סיך ניס –

וואָס טויגן מיר די ליפּעלעך שײנע,
אַז קושן, קושן זײ מיך ניס?
וואָס טויגן מיר די הענטלעך די שײנע,
אַז גלעסן, גלעסט זײ מיך ניס –

טרינק ברודער, טרינק אויס! (P. 68)

טרינק ברודער, טרינק אויס,
דאָס גלעזל ביז צום גרונט.
וועסטו וערן פֿריש און מונטער,
פֿרײלעך און געזונט.

צוזינג:
אוי, ברודערל, לחיים,
טרינק אָביסעלע וויין,
דאָס פֿאַרטרײבט די מרא שחורה,
יעדע זאָרג און פּײן.

איצט ברודער, טרינק איך,
און וואָס פֿעלט מיר אצינד?
איך פֿיל זיך גליקלעך וי אַ קעניג,
פֿרײלעך וי אַ קינד.

איצט ברודער, טרינק איך,
און וען עס רויסט אין קאָפּ,
פֿיך איך אויף דער גאַנצעל וועלט
און סאַנק מיר האָפּ-האָפּ-האָפּ!

צװײ טײבעלעך (P. 70)

צװײ טײבעלעך זײנען איבערן װאַסער
געפֿלויגן,
זײערע פֿליגעלעך האָבן זי צושפּריײז.
פֿאַרשאָלטן זאָל וערן יענער מענטש אויף
דער וועלט,
וואָס ער האָט אונדז אין אונדזער ליבע,
אוי חור, צושידעט.

און אַז דו האָסט קומען אין אַ װײסן
לאַנד, ליובעליו,
אין מײנע וערסער זאָלסטו זיך באָדענקען.
און אַז דו האָסט קומען איבער אַ סיפֿן
וואַסער, ליובעליו,
פֿאַר גרויס צרות זאָלסטו זיך ניסט
דערטרינקען.

און אַז דו האָסט קומען אין אַ װײסן
לאַנד, ליובעליו,
מײנע וערסער זאָלסטו באַקענען.
און אַז דו האָסט קומען איבער אַ גרויסן
פֿײער, ליובעליו,
פֿאַר גרויס צרות זאָלסטו זיך ניסט
פֿאַרברענגען.

צװײ טײבעלעך זײנען איבערן װאַסער
געפֿלויגן,
אין די פֿיסקעלעך האָבן זי זיך געקושט.
פֿאַרשאָלטן זאָל וערן יענער מענטש אויף
דער וועלט,
וואָס ער האָט זיך אין אונדזער ליבע,
אוי, אַרײנגעמישט.

וואַכט אויף! (P. 85)

וי לאַנג, אָ וי לאַנג וועט איר בליבן
נאָך שקלאַפֿן,
און טראַגן די שענדלעכע קייס?
וי לאַנג וועט איר גלענצענדע רײכסי-
מער שאַפֿן
פֿאַר דעם, וואָס באַרויבט אײער ברויס?

וי לאַנג וועט איר סטײן, אײער רוקן
געבויגן,
דערנידעריגט, הימלאָז, פֿאַרשמאַכט?
עס טאָגט שוין! וואַכט אויף און צו-
עפֿנט די אויגן!
דערפֿילט אײער אײזערנע מאַכט!

קלינגט אומעטום אין די פֿרײהײטס-
גלאָק!
פֿאַרזאַמעלט די לײדנדע קנעכט!
און קעמפֿט באַגײסטערט, און קעמפֿט
אומדערשראָקן,
פֿאַר אײער הײליגע רעכט!

און אַלעס וואָס וועט לעבן, און ליבן,
און בליען,
אין פֿרייהן, אין גאָלדענעם מאַין
ברידערן! געניונג פֿאַר סיראַנען צו
קניען,
שווערט, אַז איר מוזט פֿרײ ווערן פֿרײ!

(P. 60) שלאָף מיין קינד, מיין טרייסט, מיין
שינער

לערנט קינדער, האָט ניט מורא,
יעדער אָנהויב איז שווער,
גליקלעך דער וואָס האָט געלערנט
תּורה,
צי דאַרף דער מענטש נאָך מער?

איר וועט קינדער, עלטער ווערן,
וועט איר אַלין פֿאַרשטין,
וויפֿיל אין די אותיות ליגן טרערן,
און וויפֿיל געוויין.

אַז איר וועט קינדער, דעם גלות
שלעפֿן,
אויסגעמוטשעט זיין,
זאָלט איר פֿון די אותיות כּח שעפּן,
קוקט אין זי אַרין!

שלאָף מיין קינד, מיין טרייסט, מיין
שינער
שלאָף-זשע זונעניו,
שלאָף מיין קינד, מיין קדיש אינער,
שלאָף-זשע ליוליוליו.

בי דיין וויגל, זיצט דיין מאַמע,
זינגט אַ ליד און וויינט,
וועסט אַמאָל פֿאַרשטין מסתּמא,
וואָס זי האָט געמינט.

אין אַמעריקע איז דער סאַסע,
דינער, זונעניו,
דו ביזט נאָך אַ קינד, לעת-עתה,
שלאָף-זשע, ליוליוליו.

אין אַמעריקע איז פֿאַר יעדן,
זאָגט מען, גאָר אַ גליק,
און פֿאַר יעדן, אַ גן-עדן,
גאָר עפּעס אַן אַנסיק.

דאָרטן עסט מען אין דער וואָכן
חלה, זונעניו,
יאַיכעלעך וועל איך דיר קאָכן
שלאָף-זשע, שלאָף, ליוליו.

ער וועט שיקן צוואַנציג דאָלאַר,
זיין פּאָרטרעט דערצו,
און וועט נעמען, לעבן זאָל ער,
אונדז אַהינצוצו.

ער וועט כאַפֿן אונדז און קושן,
טאַנצן אַזש פֿאַר פֿרייד,
איך וועל קוואַלן טרערן גיסן,
וויינען שטילערהייט.

ביז עס קומט דאָס גוטע קוויטל,
שלאָף-זשע זונעניו,
שלאָפֿן איז אַ סיער מיסל,
שלאָף-זשע, ליוליוליו.

פּאַפּיר איז דאָך ווייס (P. 58)

פּאַפּיר איז דאָך ווייס און סינט איז
דאָך שוואַרץ,
צו דיר מיין זיס-לעבן, ציט דאָך מיין
האַרץ.
איך וואָלט שטענדיק געזעסן, דרי טעג
נאָכאַנאַנד,
צו קושן דיר, דיין פּנים און צו האַלטן
דיין האַנד.

נעכטן בין איך אויף אַ חתונה געווען,
פֿיל שינע מיידעלעך האָב איך דאָרט
געזען.
אי, פֿיל שינע מיידעלעך, צו דיר קומט
ניט גאָר,
מיט דיינע שוואַרצע אייגעלעך און מיט
דיינע שוואַרצע האָר.

אָך דו ליבער גאָט, הער אויס מיין
פֿאַרלאַנג,
דעם עושר גיסטו כּבֿוד, מיס אַ שינעם
גאַנג,
אוי, מיר גיב אַ שטיבעלע אויף דעם
גראָז דעם גרינעם,
און איך מיט מיין זיס-לעבן זאָל
וואָוינען דערינען.

שלאָף מיין קינד, שלאָף כּסדר (P. 67)

שלאָף מיין קינד, שלאָף כּסדר,
זינגען וועל איך דיר אַ ליד,
אַז דו, מיין קינד, וועסט עלטער ווערן,
וועסטו וויסן אַן אונטערשיד.

אַז דו, מיין קינד, וועסט עלטער ווערן,
וועסטו ווערן מיט לייסן גליך,
דעמאָלס וועסטו געוואָויר ווערן,
וואָס הייסט אָרים און וואָס הייסט רייך.

די שענסטע פּאַלאַצן, די פֿיינסטע הייזער,
דאָס אַלץ מאַכט דער אָרימאַן,
נאָר ווייסטו ווער עס וואוינען זיי?
גאָר ניט ער, נאָר דער רייכער מאַן.

דער אָרימאַן, ער וואוינט אין קעלער,
דער וויליאַסס רינט אים פֿון די וואַנט.
דערפֿון באַקומט ער רעמאַטיז פֿעלער,
אין די פֿיס און אין די הענט.

שין בין איך, שין (P. 66)

שין בין איך, שין
שין איז אויך מיין נאָמען,
רעדט מען מיר שידוכים
מיס גרויסע רבנים.

רבנישע תּורה
איז דאָך זייער גרויס,
בין איך בי מיין מאַמען
אַ ליכסיגע רויז.

אַ שין מיידעלע בין איך,
בלויע זעקעלעך טראָג איך,
געלט אין די טאַשן,
ביר אין די פֿלאַשן.

חיין אין די קריגעלעך,
קינדער אין די חינעלעך,
שרייען חי די ציגעלעך:
מע, מע, מע!

מאכט ער מיר א סרובעצקע,
די סרובעצקע מאכט אזוי:
סרוטרוטרו, סרוטרוסרו,
אזוי מאכט די סרובעצקע!

מאכט ער מיר א צימבעלע,
דאָס צימבעלע מאכט אזוי:
צימצימצים, צימצימצים,
ווזוי מאכט דאָס צימבעלע!

(P. 50) אָט אזוי נייט א שניידער

צוזינג:
אָט אזוי נייט א שניידער,
אָט אזוי נייט ער דאָך.

ער ניט און ניט א גאנצע וואָך,
פאַרדינט א גילדן מיט א לאָך.

א שניידער נייט און ניט און ניט,
פאַרדינט קדחות, ניט קיין ברויט.

פאראיאָרן, ניט היינט געדאכט,
האָבן מיר געהאַרעוועט פון אכט ביז
אכט.

אבער די סטרוקציע* האָט געמאכט,
מיר האַרעווען שוין מער ניט פון
אכט ביז אכט.

* א פאַרקירצונג פון דעם וואָרט:
אבסטרוקציע.

(P. 52) אוי, א נאכט א שיינע

אוי, א נאכט א שיינע,
די נאכט איז געווען אזוי שיין.
אויף א בענקעלע זיינען מיר געזעסן,
די לבנה האָט געגומען אהעגינ.

אויף א בענקעלע זיינען מיר געזעסן,
און האָבן צוזאמען פאַרבראכס.
חיפיל רייד מיר האָבן אימנג'סטעגה״ס,
צו קיין סאָלק האָבן מיר זיך ניט
דערטראכס.

וואָס-זשע פארא סאָלק ליבע, ווילסטו?
אז איך מוז צו דעם פרידזיח שטיין.
קיין קנס-מאל קענען מיר ניט מאכן,
דאָס קענסטו דאָך אליין פארשטיין.

אויף באנען וועל איך פאָרן,
און אויף וואסערן שווימען צו דיר.
כ׳וועל פאַרלאָזן פאַטער און מוטער,
און קומען, זיס-לעבן, צו דיר.

אויף קיין באנען זאָלסטו ניט פאָרן,
און אויף וואסערן זאָלסטו ניט שווימען
צו מיר.
א חופה, אוי דושעניו, לאָמיר שטעלן,
און אין דריי יאָר וועל איך קומען צו
דיר.

(P. 54) אוי דאָרטן, דאָרטן, איבערן וואסערל

אוי, דאָרטן, דאָרטן, איבערן וואסערל,
אוי, דאָרטן, דאָרטן, איבערן בריק.

פאָרסריבן האָסטו מיך אין די ווייטענע
לענדער,
און בענקען, בענק איך נאָך דיר
צוריק.

אוי, וויפיל אָהנסלעך, צוזאמען
געדעקסן,
אוי, וויפיל אָהנסלעך, שפעט אין דער
נאכס.
אוי, וויפיל סרעלעלעך, מיר האָבן
פאַרגאָסן,
ביז מיר האָבן די ליבע צוזא־
מענגעבראכס.

אוי, דיינע אויגעלעך, ווי די שווארצע
קאַרשעלעך,
דיינע ליפעלעך, ווי די ראָזעווע
פאפיר,
און דיינע פינגערלעך, ווי סינט און
ווי פעדער,
אוי, שרייבן זאָלסטו אָפטס בריוו צו
מיר.

(P. 51) אויפן באַרג און איבערן באַרג

אויפן באַרג און איבערן באַרג,
פליען סויבן פאָרן,
נאָך קיין נחת ניט דערלעבט,
שוין אחוק די יאָרן.

לאָמיר שפאַנען פערד און וואָגן,
לאָמיר לויפן, פאָרן,
אפשר וועלן מיר דעריאָגן
אובדזערע יונגע יאָרן.

שוין דעריאָגס די יונגע יאָרן,
אויפן הויכן בריק.
יאָרן, יאָרן, קערס זיך אום,
כאָטש אין נעסט צוריק!

ניין, מיר וועלן זיך ניט אומקערן,
ס׳איז ניטאָ צו וועמען.
האָס איר פריער ניט באדארפס
אודבדז אזוי פאַרשפעמען!

(P. 56) אויפן פריפעטשאק ברענט א פייערל

אויפן פריפעטשאק ברענט א פייערל,
און אין שטוב איז הייס,
און דער רבי בי לערנט קליינע קינדערלעך
דעם אלף-בית.

צוזינג:
זעט-זשע קינדערלעך, געדענקט-זשע
סירעלע,
וואָס איר לערנס דא.
זאָגט-זשע נאָך אמאָל און טאקע נאָך
אמאָל:
קמץ-אלף: אָ!

לערנט קינדער, מיט גרויס חשק,
אזוי זאָג איך אייך אָן.
ווער ס׳וועט גיכער פון אייך קענען
עברי,
דער באקומס א פאָן.

90

צוזינג:
סאַנק, סאַנק, אַנטקעגן מיר,
און איך אַנטקעגן דיר –
דו העסט נעמען דעם אײדים
און איך װעל נעמען די שנירן

צעבראָכן איז דער לאָקשנטאָפּ,
פֿאַרברענט דער נאַהיט –
סאַנצן די מחתנת'סעס,
די כּלה אין דער מיס.

חתן'ס צד און כּלה'ס צד –
די גאַנצע משפּחה –
סאַנצן אויף דער חתונה
אין מזל און אין ברכה!

(P. 44) לאָמיר זיך איבערבעטן

לאָמיר זיך איבערבעטן, איבערבעטן,
װאָס שטייסטו בײַ דער טיר?
לאָמיר זיך איבערבעטן,
קום אַרײן צו מיר.

לאָמיר זיך איבערבעטן, איבערבעטן,
װאָס שטײסטו בײַ מײן פֿענסטער?
לאָמיר זיך איבערבעטן,
בײַזט בײַ מיר דער שענסטער.

לאָמיר זיך איבערבעטן, איבערבעטן,
קויף אַ פּאָר מאָראנצן,
לאָמיר זיך איבערבעטן,
לאָמיר גיען סאַנצן.

לאָמיר זיך איבערבעטן, איבערבעטן,
שטעל דעם סאַמאָװאַר!
לאָמיר זיך איבערבעטן,
זײ-זשע נישט קײן נאַר.

לאָמיר זיך איבערבעטן, איבערבעטן,
לאָמיר נישט זײן חי גרים.
לאָמיר זיך איבערבעטן,
לאָמיר זײן חברים.

(P. 45) גײ איך מיר שפּאַצירן

גײ איך מיר שפּאַצירן, טראַלאַלאַ, לאַלאַלאַ
גײ איך מיר שפּאַצירן, טראַלאַלאַ,
לאַלאַלאַ, לאַ.

באַגעגנט זיך אַ בחור, אַהאַ, אַהאַ,
באַגעגנט זיך אַ בחור, אַהאַ!

ער זאַגט ער װעט זיך נעמען...
ער לײינט עס אַפ אויף װײַנטער...

דער װײַנטער איז געקומען...
ער האָט זיך ניט גענומען...

איצט װיל ער זיך שוין נעמען...
אַבער איך װיל אים ניט קענען!...

(P. 46) מײן אינגעלע

איך האָב אַ קלײנעם אינגעלע
אַ זונעלע גאָר פֿײן.
װען איך דערזע אים,דאַכט זיך מיר,
די גאַנצע װעלט איז מײן.

נאַר זעלטן, זעלטן, זע איך אים,
מײַן שײנעם חען ער װאַכס.
איך טרעף אים אימער שלאָפֿענדיג,
איך זע אים נאָר בײַנאַכס.

די אַרבעט טרײַבט מיך פֿרי אַרויס,
און לאָזט מיך שפּעט צוריק.
אַ פֿרעמד איז מיר מײַן אײגן לײַב,
אַ פֿרעמד, מײַן קינד'ס אַ בליק.

איך קום צוקלעמטערהייט אַהיים,
אין פֿינצטערניש געהילט,
מײַן בלײכע פֿרוי דערצײלט מיר באַלד,
װי פֿײַן דאָס קינד זיך שפּילט.

װי זיס עס רעדט, װי קלוג עס פֿרעגט:
אָ מאַמע, גוטע מאַ,
װען קומט און ברענגט אַ פּעני מיר,
מײַן גוטער, גוטער פּאַ?

איך הער עס צו, און יאָ, עס מוז,
יאָ, יאָ, עס מוז געשעען,
די פֿאַטער-ליבע פֿלאַקערט אויף,
עס מוז מײַן קינד מיך זען!

איך שטײ בײַ זײַן געלעגערל,
און הער און זע און שאָ.
אַ טרוים באַװעגט די ליפעלעך:
אָ װאו איז, װאו איז פּאַ?

איך קוש די בלויע אויגעלעך,
זײ עפֿענען זיך, אָ קינד!
זײ זעען מיך, זײ זעען מיך!
און שליסן זיך געשװינד.

דאָ שטײט דײן פּאַפּאַ, טײַערער,
אַ פּעניגעלע דיר, נאָ!
אַ טרוים באַװעגט די ליפעלעך:
אָ װאו איז, װאו איז פּאַ?

איך בלײַב צעחושטאַגט און צוקלעמט,
פֿאַרביטערט, און איך קלער:
װען דו ערװאַכסט אַמאָל, מײן קינד,
געפֿינסטו מיך ניט מער...

(P. 48) מיכאַלקו

צוזינג:
האָב איך מיר אַ קלײנעם מיכאַלקו,
מיכאַלקו,
חאָװינט ער אויף דער לאַנגער גאַס.
מאַכט ער מיר חאָס ער װיל,
מאַכט ער מיר חאָס ער קען:

מאַכט ער מיר אַ פֿיקעלע,
דאָס פֿיקעלע מאַכט אַזוי:
סאָראָבאָבאַבאַם, סאָראָבאָבאַבאַם,
אַזוי מאַכט דאָס פֿיקעלע!

מאַכט ער מיר אַ פֿימפעלע,
דאָס פֿימפעלע מאַכט אַזוי:
פֿלופֿלופֿלו, פֿלופֿלופֿלו,
אַזוי מאַכט דאָס פֿימפעלע!

מאַכט ער מיר אַ פֿידעלע,
דאָס פֿידעלע מאַכט אַזוי:
פֿידל-דידל-דידל, לידל-דידל-דידל,
אַזוי מאַכט דאָס פֿידעלע!

אין ליד סטענדיג הונגער,
איך האב ניט וואס צו עסן,
וויל איך גולט בעסן,
הרעסט מען מיר פארגעסן.

(P. 34) אײן כלו אין כלו אין כל זײַן

אין כל, אין כל, אין כל זײַן...
כ׳קאן אן דיר ניט זײַן.

אין כל, אין כל, אין כל ביר...
כ׳קאן ניט זײַן אן דיר.

אין כל, אין כל, אין כל יש...
כ׳וויל א פולע פלאש.

אין כל, אין כל, אין כל קאניאק...
אײ, איז דאס געסמאק.

אין כל, אין כל, אין כל קוואס...
כ׳וויל א פולע פאס.

(P. 36) גיבן דיר מײן טאכטער

גיבן דיר מײן טאכטער, גיבן דיר מײן
טאכטער.
א שוסטער פאר א מאן? א שוסטער פאר
א מאן?
-א שוסטער פאר א מאן, וויל איך ניט,
א שוסטער׳ס א טאכטער בין איך ניט,
לאסט שטיחל קאן איך ניט.

ערסטער צוזינגג:
זיך איך אויף א שטרין,
און קוק ארא... און חין,
און זע חי אלע מידעלעך האבן חתונה,
און נאר איך בלײב אלין.

גיבן דיר מײן טאכטער...
א שנידער פאר א מאן?...
-א שנידער פאר א מאן, וויל איך ניט,
א שנידער׳ס א טאכטער בין איך ניט,
נײען קליידער קאן איך ניט.

ערסטער צוזינגג:
גיבן דיר מײן טאכטער...
א לומדן פאר א מאן?...
-א לומד׳ס א טאכטער, בין איך יא!
א לומד׳ס א טאכטער, בין איך יא!
תורה לערנען קאן איך יא!

צווײטער צוזינגג:
זיך איך אויפן דאך,
און קוק ארא... און לאך,
און זע חי אלע מידעלעך האבן חתונה,
און איך בין מיט זי גלײַך!

(P. 38) האב איך א פאר אקסן

האב איך א פאר אקסן, אקסן,
וואס זי בראקן לאקשן, לאקשן,
אי וואונדער איבער וואונדער,
חי די אקסן בראקן לאקשן,
דאס איז מיר א וואונדער,
דאס איז מיר א וואונדער!

האב איך א פאר בערן, בערן,
וואס זי שטיבער קערן, קערן,
אי וואונדער איבער וואונדער,
חי די בערן שטיבער קערן,
און די אקסן בראקן לאקשן, א.א.ח.

האב איך א פאר ציגן, ציגן,
וואס זי קינדער חיגן, חיגן.
אי וואונדער איבער וואונדער,
חי די ציגן קינדער חיגן,
און די בערן שטיבער קערן,
און די אקסן בראקן לאקשן,א.א.ח.

האב איך א פאר הינט, הינט,
וואס זי מאכן סינט, סינט.
אי וואונדער איבער וואונדער,
חי די הינט מאכן סינט,
און די ציגן קינדער חיגן,
און די בערן שטיבער קערן,
און די אקסן בראקן לאקשן,א.א.ח.

האב איך א פאר הענער, הענער,
וואס זי קליבן שפענער, שפענער.
אי וואונדער איבער וואונדער,
חי די הענער קליבן שפענער,
און די הינט מאכן סינט,
און די ציגן קינדער חיגן,
און די בערן שטיבער קערן,
און די אקסן בראקן לאקשן,
דאס איז מיר א וואונדער,
דאס איז מיר א וואונדער!

(P. 40) האפ מינע המנטאשן

יאקנע-דחאשע פארס אין מארק,
זי האלס זיך אין אין פאק,
פארס אויף פורים קויפן מעל,
המנטאשן באקן.

צוזינגג:
האפ, מינע המנטאשן,
האפ, מינע חײסע!
האפ, מיט מינע המנטאשן
האט פאסירס א מעשה!

ס׳גיס א רעגן, ס׳גיס א שנר,
ס׳קאפעט פון די דעכער,
יאקנע פירס שוין קאראמעל,
אין א זאק מיס לעכער.

ניס קין האניג, ניס קין מעל,
און פארגעסן היחן,
יאקנע מאכס שוין המנטאשן,
ס׳באקט זיך שוין אין אויחן.

יאקנע פירס שוין שלח-מנות,
צו דער באבע יענטע,
צחיי-דרי המנטאשן,
האלב-רוי, האלב-פארברענטע.

(P. 42) האט זיך מיר די זים צעזיפט

האט זיך מיר די זים צעזיפט
און האט זיך מיר צעבראכן.
האט זיך מיר די זיך צעריסן,
טאנץ איך אין די הוילע זאקן!

חאצקעלע, חאצקעלע (P. 25)

חאצקעלע, חאצקעלע,
שפּיל מיר אַ קאַזאַצקעלע,
כאַטש אַן אָרעמע,
אַבי אַ כוואַסקעץ.

צוזינג:
אָרים איז ניט גוט,
אָרים איז ניט גוט.
לאָמיר זיך ניט שעמען
מיט אירגענע בלוט.

ניט קיין גענבסטענע,
אַליין געקרומע.
כאַטש אַן אָרעמע,
פאַרט, אַ פרומע!

חאצקעלע, חאצקעלע,
שפּיל מיר אַ רומע,
כאַטש אַן אָרעמע,
אַבי אַ פרומען!

דרעמלען פיגל אויף די צווייגן (P. 26)

דרעמלען פיגל אויף די צווייגן,
שלאָף מיין טייער קינד,
ביי דיין וויגל, אויף דיין נאָרע,
זיצט אַ פרעמדע און זינגט:
ליוליו, ליוליו, ליו.

ס'איז דיין וויגל חאו געשטאנען
אויסגעפלאָכטן פון גליק.
און דיין מאמע, אוי דיין מאמע,
קומט שוין קיינמאָל ניט צוריק.
ליוליו, ליוליו, ליו.

כ'האב געזען דיין טאטן לויפן
אונטער האגל פון שטיין.
איבער פעלדער איז געפלויגן
זיין פאַר'יתום'טער געוויין.
ליוליו, ליוליו, ליו.

דו מיידעלע דו פיינס, דו מיידעלע דו שיינס (P. 28)

דו מיידעלע דו פיינס, דו מיידעלע דו שיינס,
איך וועל דיר עפעס פרעגן, אַ רעטעניש אַ קליינס,
וואָס איז העכער פון אַ הויז?
און וואָס איז פלינקער פון אַ מויז?

דו נאַרישער בחור, דו נאַרישער קלאָץ!
האָסט דען ניט קיין שכל אין דיין קאָפּ!
-דער רויך איז העכער פון אַ הויז,
אַ קאַץ איז פלינקער פון אַ מויז.

דו מיידעלע דו פיינס, דו מיידעלע דו שיינס,
איך וועל דיר עפעס פרעגן, אַ רעטעניש אַ קליינס:
וואָס פליס אָן אַ פיגל?
און וואָס מויערס אָן אַ ציגל?

דו נאַרישער בחור, דו נאַרישער קלאָץ!
האָסט דען ניט קיין שכל אין דיין קאָפּ!
-דער שניי פליס אָן אַ פליגל,
דער פראָסט מויערס אָן אַ ציגל.

דו מיידעלע דו פיינס, דו מיידעלע דו שיינס,
איך וועל דיר עפעס פרעגן, אַ רעטעניש אַ קליינס:
וואָס פאַרא קיסר איז אָן אַ לאַנד?
און וואָס פאַרא וואַסער איז אָן אַ זאַמד?

דו נאַרישער בחור, דו נאַרישער קלאָץ!
האָסט דען ניט קיין שכל אין דיין קאָפּ!
-דער קיסר פון קאָרטן האָסט ניט קיין לאַנד
טרערן פון די אויגן זיינען אָן אַ זאַמד.

עס איז געפלויגן די גילדערנע פאווע (P. 30)

איז געפלויגן די גילדערנע פאווע,
איבער אַלע ימען,
לאָז גריסן, דו גילדערנער פויגל,
מיין ליבער, האַרציגער מאַמען.

געפלויגן, געפלויגן די גילדערנע פאווע,
איבער סיך, דעם גלאַטן.
לאָז גריסן, דו גילדערנער פויגל,
מיין ליבן, האַרציגען טאַטן.

געפלויגן, געפלויגן, די גילדערנע פאווע,
איבער אַלע פעלדער.
האָסט די פאַרלוירן דעם גילדערנעם פעדער,
אין די פרעמדע לענדער.

ניט אזוי די גילדערנע פעדער,
ווי די פאווע אַליין.
ניט אזוי דער פרעמדער זון,
ווי די סאָכטער אַליין.

ווי עס איז ביטער, מיין ליבע מוטער,
אַ וואַסער אָן אַ פיש.
אזוי איז ביטער, מיין ליבע מוטער,
ביי אַ פרעמדן טיש.

ווי עס איז ביטער, מיין ליבע מוטער,
אַ פייגעלע אָן אַ נעסט.
אזוי איז ביטער, מיין ליבע מוטער,
שווער און שוויגער'ס קעסט.

אידער איך ליג מיך שלאָפן (P. 32)

אידער איך ליג מיך שלאָפן,
דאַרף איך שוין אויפשטיין,
מיט מיינע קראַנקע ביינער,
צו דער אַרבעט גרין.

צוזינג:
צו גאָט וועל איך וויינען,
מיט גרויס געוויין:
וואָס בין איך געבוירן
אַ נישטאַרין צו זיין?

כ'קום שפעט צו דער אַרבעס,
ס'איז דאָך חיט דער וועג,
שלאָגט מען מיר אָפּ
פאַר האלבע טעג.

די נאָדלען ווערן צעבראָכן
פּופצן אַ מינוט,
די פינגער ווערן צעשטאָכן,
עס רינט פון זיי דאָס בלוט.

בײַט-זשע מיר אויס א פינף-און-
צוואנציקער,
אויף סאמע אימפעריאלן,
איך וועל בעטן די קליזמרים׳לעך,
זײ זאָלן זיך ניט אײלן.

(P. 13) בין איך מיר א שנײַדערל

בין איך מיר א שנײַדערל,
לעב איך מיר טאָג אויס, טאָג אײַן,
לוסטיק און פרײלעך און פײַן.
-זאָג מיר שנײַדער, ליבינקער און גוטער,
גיט דיר די נאָדל, גענוג אויף ברויט
מיט פּוטער?
-איך מאַך א וואָן, צוויי גילדן מיט א
דרײער,
איך עס נאַר ברויט, ווײַל פּוטער איז
צו טײַער.

בין איך מיר א שוסטערל,
לעב איך מיר טאָג אויס, טאָג אײַן,
לוסטיק און פרײלעך און פײַן.
-זאָג מיר שוסטער, האָסטו וואָס צו
קײען?
פעלט דיר אויוסעט, האָסטו וואו צו
לײען?
-קײנער לײַס ניט, קינדער גיט קײן
צרבות,
איך בין א שוסטער, גײ איך סאָקע
באָרוועס.

בין איך מיר א בלעכערל,
לעב איך מיר טאָג אויס, טאָג אײַן,
לוסטיק און פרײלעך און פײַן.
-זאָג מיר בלעכער, ווי גרויס איז בײַ
דיר די נויט?
האָסטו בולקעס, האָסטו ניט קײן
ברויט?
-איך זיץ און קלאַפ בײַ יענעם פרעמדע
דעכער,
בײַ מיר אין סטוב רינט פון אַלע לעכער.

בין איך מיר א קרעמערל,
לעב איך מיר טאָג אויס, טאָג אײַן,
לוסטיק און פרײלעך און פײַן.
-זאָג מיר קרעמער, האָסטו מיט וואָס צו
האַנדלען?
האָסטו אין קרעמל ראַזשינקעס מיט
מאַנדלען?
-איך האָב אין קרעמל פאר צוויי גראשן
סחורה,
איך שלעפ דעם דלות און איך בענטש
דעם בורא.

(P. 20) בין איך מיר געגאנגען פישעלעך קויפן

בין איך מיר געגאנגען פישעלעך
קויפן,
האָב איך מיר געקויפּס א העכט.
און ווער עס איז שולדיג אין אונדזער
ליבע,
דער זאָל אויסגײען ווי א ליכט!

צוזינג: די די די...
אַז א קאַרטיאָזשניק שפּילט אין קאָרטן,
פאַרשפּילט ער דאָך נאָר זײַן געלט.
איך האָב פאַרשפּילט מײַנע יונגע יאָרן,
מײַנסטער איז דאָך מײַן וועלט.

אָן קײן ציגל און אָן קײן שטײנער,
קאָן מען קײן הויז ניט בויערן,
אַי, ס׳איז ניטשטאָ אזאַ מענטש אויף
דער וועלט,
וואָס ער זאָל מיך ניט באַדויערן!

(P. 22) בײזסטו מיט מיר ברוגז

בײזסטו מיט מיר ברוגז
ווײַס איך ניט פארוואָס?
גײסט אַרום א גאַנצן טאָג
אראָפּגעלאָזט די נאָז.

צוזינג: די די די....
און אפשר ווילסטו וויסן
אַז איך האָב דיך ליב?
לאָמיר בײדע אריבערפאָרן
צו דעם גוטן ייד.

צו דעם גוטן ייד
א פדיון אים אָפּגעבן,
וועט ער פאר אונדז גאָט בעטן
פאר א גוט לעבן.

און אַז מיר וועלן קומען
צוריק פון גוטן ייד,
וועלן מיר בײדע אריבערפאָרן
אין זעלוט אויף דעם יריד.

דאָרט וועל איך דיר קויפן
א זײגער מיט א קײט,
און א שײנע גרויס שטיק
זײדענס אויף א קלײד.

טאַ, זײַ-זשע מער ניטא ברוגז
און גרײט אויף גיך צום טיש -
און זעץ זיך מיט מיר עסן,
באַקומסטו פון מיר א קוש!

(P. 24) בולבעס

זונטיק - בולבעס,
מאָנטיק - בולבעס,
דינסטיק און מיטוואָך - בולבעס,
דאָנערשטיק און פרײַטיק - בולבעס.
אָבער שבת אין א נאָווינע, א בולבע
קוגעלע!
און זונטיק ווײַטער, בולבעס.

ברויט מיט בולבעס,
פלײש מיט בולבעס,
וואַרימעס און וועטשערע - בולבעס,
אָבער און ווידער - בולבעס.
אָבער אײנמאל אין א נאָווינע, א בולבע
קוגעלע!
און זונטיק ווײַטער, בולבעס.

אָבער - בולבעס,
ווידער - בולבעס,
אָבער און ווידער - בולבעס,
ווידער און אָבער - בולבעס.
אָבער שבת נאָכן טשאָלנט, א בולבע
קוגעלע!
און זונטיק ווײַטער, בולבעס.

(P. 10) אַמאָל איז געווען אַ מעשה

אַמאָל איז געווען אַ מעשה,
די מעשה איז גאָרניט פריילעך,
די מעשה הױבט זיך אָנעט
מיט אַ ייִדישן מלך.

צוזינג:
ליולינקע מײַן פֿײגעלע,
ליולינקע מײַן קינד.
כ׳האָב אָנגעװאָירן אַזאַ ליבע,
װי איז מיר און װינד.

דער מלך האָט געהאַט אַ מלכה,
די מלכה האָט געהאַט אַ װײנגאָרטן,
דער װײנגאָרטן האָט געהאַט אַ בוים,
ליולינקע מײַן קינד.

דער בוים האָט געהאַט אַ צװײג,
דער צװײג האָט געהאַט אַ נעסטעלע,
אין נעסטעלע איז געהאַט אַ פֿייגעלע,
ליולינקע מײַן קינד.

דער מלך איז אָפּגעשטאָרבן,
די מלכה איז געװאָרן פֿאַרדאָרבן,
דער צװײג איז אָפּגעבראָכן,
דאָס פֿייגעלע פֿון נעסט אַנטלאָפֿן.

װאו נעמט מען אַזאַ חכם,
ער זאָל קענען די שטערן ציילן?
װאו נעמט מען אַזאַ דאָקטער,
ער זאָל קענען מײַן האַרץ הײלן?

(P. 12) אײליע ליוליע ליוליע

אײליע ליוליע ליוליע,
שלאָף־זשע, שלאָף מײַן גדולה,
מאַך־זשע צו דײַנע
אייגעלעך, די פֿײנע.

און שטײ אױף װידער,
מיט געזונטע גלידער,
מײַן ליב־זיס קינד,
גיך און געשװינד.

אין מאַרק װעל איך לױפֿן,
בײגעלעך װעל איך קױפֿן,
מיט פּוטער װעל איך שמירן,
צו דער חופה זאָל איך דיך פֿירן...

װעסט אױסװאַקסן אַ גרױסינקער,
װעסטו זײַן אַ תנא!
װעלן דאָך אַלע
זײַן מיר מקנא!

(P. 16) בײַ דעם שטעטל שטײט אַ שטיבל

בײַ דעם שטעטל שטײט אַ שטיבל,
מיט אַ גרינעם דאַך,
און אַרום דעם שטיבל װאַקסן
בײמעלעך אַ סך.

און דער סאָסע מיט דער מאַמע,
חנהלע מיט מיר,
שױן אַ לאַנגע צײַט אינאײנעם
װאױינען אַלע פיר.

און דער סאָסע האָרעװעט, האָרעװעט,
אַלע יאָרן זײַנע,
און ער קױפֿט אונדז, און ער ברענגט
אונדז
זאַכן שײנע, פֿײנע.

ברענגט אַ הינטעלע, װאָס סע האַװקעט,
מיסן נאָמען צוציק.
ברענגט אַ פֿערדל װאָס סע הירזשעט,
מיסן נאָמען מוזיק.

ברענגט אַ געגנדזעלע מיס אַ לאַנגן האַלדז
פֿעדערלעך װײַס חי שני,
ברענגט אַ הון װאָס קװאָקעט, קװאָקעט,
ביז זי לייגט אַן אײ!

נעמסט די מאַמע, אַס די אײער,
אַיי, איז דאָס אַ מתּנה!
זעצט זי זיך אױף אַ קװאָקע,
האָבן מיר ניע צופּות!

(P. 17) אױפֿן ים זיצט אַ זינטעלע

אױפֿן ים זיצט אַ װינטעלע,
און די כװאַליעס שלאָגן.
איך האָב זיך פֿאַרליבט אין אַ שײן
אינגעלע,
כ׳האָב ניט פֿאַר װעמען צו זאָגן.

איך האָב זיך געבאָװעט אַ שטיבעלע
אין װאַלד,
אַרום און אַרום מיט פֿענסטער,
פֿון אַלע קאָרטינקעס װאָס איך האָב
געזען,
ביזטו בײַ מיר דער שענסטער!

צו ליבסטו מיך פֿון טיפֿן האַרצן,
צו ליבסטו נאָר מײַן שײן פּנים?
דו האָסט מיך גאָר אױסגעקױלעט,
אַזױ װי די רעכטע גזלנים!

אַז אַ גזלן קױלעט אַ מענטשן,
קױלעט ער אים מיט אַ מעסער.
האָסט מיך געקױלעט, און נישט
דערקױלעט,
ביזט פֿון אַ גזלן נאָך גרעסער!

(P. 18) בײַט־זשע מיר אױס אַ פֿינף־און־צוואַנציקער

בײַט־זשע מיר אױס אַ פֿינף־און־
צוואַנציקער,
אױף סאַמאָראָדנע פֿירער,
און שפּילט־זשע מיר קלעזמירים׳לעך,
דאָס זעלביקע חי פֿריִער.

צוזינג:
רימטשי׳... ראַם.

בײַט־זשע מיר אױס אַ פֿינף־און־
צוואַנציקער,
אױף סאַמאָראָדנע דרײַער,
און שפּילט־זשע מיר קלעזמירים׳לעך,
אַ לידעלע אַ טײַער.

בײַט־זשע מיר אױס אַ פֿינף־און־
צוואַנציקער,
אױף סאַמאָראָדנע צענער,
און שפּילט־זשע מיר קלעזמירים׳לעך,
דאָס זעלביקע נאָך שענער.

YIDDISH TEXTS

(P. 6) א גנבה

צוזינג:

בײַ מיַן רבין איז געוועזן,
איז געוועזן, בײַ מיַן רבין.
בײַ מיַן רבין איז געוועזן – א גנבה!

זיבן העמדער ווי די בעכער,
דרײַ מיט לאַטעס, פיר מיט לעכער.
בײַ מיַן רבין איז געוועזן.
א גנבה!

צוזינג:

זיבן לײַכטער ווי די בערן,
דרײַ אן פיס און פיר אן רערן.
בײַ מיַן רבין איז געוועזן.
א גנבה!

צוזינג:

זיבן הענער ווי די זיגל,
דרײַ אן קעפ און פיר אן פליגל.
בײַ מיַן רבין איז געוועזן.
א גנבה!

צוזינג:

זיבן סעקטער ווי די סאָסנעס,
דרײַ אן צײן און פיר אן יאסלעס.
בײַ מיַן רבין איז געוועזן.
א גנבה!

(P. 8) אױף די פעלדער, גרינע פעלדער

אױף די פעלדער, גרינע פעלדער, אױ־חײ,
אױף די פעלדער, גרינע פעלדער,
דאָרט ליגט פארװאָרפן א יונגער זעלנער,
אױ־חײ.
דאָרט ליגט פארװאָרפן א יונגער זעלנער,
אױ־חײ.

קומט א פויגל אָן צופליען, אױ־חײ.
אױף זיַן קבר אָפצורוען, אױ־חײ.

אױ דו פויגל, פלי געשװינד,
און זאָג דער מאַמען איך בין געזונט.

פון דעם סויס זאָלסטו איר ניט זאָגן,
ווײַל זי וועט נעבעך וױנען און קלאָגן.

קומט דער פויגל צופליען אהים,
און טרעפט זיַן מאַמען טרויעריק זיצן.

ווי איז מיר, אױ ווי און װינד!
ס'האָט פארסריבן מיַן אינציק קינד!

װען די מאמד חעס צערונגען װערן,
וועט זיך צו מיר מיַן קינד אומקערן.

װען די מאמד װעט אמאל אנסריגען,
איר קינד װעט שױן אהים ניט קומען.

(P. 9) אלע װאסערלעך פליסן אװעק

אלע װאסערלעך פליסן אװעק,
די גריבעלעך בליַבן לידיק.
ניטאָ אזא מענטש אױף גאָר דער װעלט,
װאָס'זאָל פארשטײן מיַן װײטיג.

די יאָרעלעך ציען, די יאָרעליך פליען,
די ציַט גיט אװעק ווי רויך,
און אז איך דערמאָן זיך אָן מיַר, מיַן
זיס־לעבן,
גיט מיר אױס דער כח.

און אז א מידעלע שפילט א ליבע,
שפילן אין איר אלע פארבן,
און אז זי שפילט איר ליבע ניט אױס,
קאָן זי חלילה נאָך שטארבן.

און אז די טעפעלעך טריקענען אױס,
בלײַבן זי אלע לידיק,
און אז א מידעלע פירט איר ליבע ניט
אױס,
װערט זי פארפאלן אױף אײביג.